two
new ships
one
new era

P&O Ferries' **Spirit *of* Britain**
and **Spirit *of* France**

John Hendy

Published by:
Ferry Publications, PO Box 33, Ramsey, Isle of Man IM99 4LP

Tel: +44 (0) 1624 898445   Fax: +44 (0) 1624 898449

E-mail: ferrypubs@manx.net   Website: www.ferrypubs.co.uk

P&O Ferries

Foreword

by Helen Deeble
Chief Executive Officer

Welcome to 'Two New Ships, One New Era', specially commissioned by P&O Ferries to commemorate the introduction of *Spirit of Britain* and *Spirit of France* to the Dover Strait.

Taking delivery of new vessels is always an exciting time for the crews and shore employees of shipping companies, particularly when the ships concerned are revolutionary in so many aspects of their design, and at P&O Ferries we are all thrilled and immensely proud to have been part of the process that has led to the creation and launching of our new cross-Channel sisters.

Our in-house project team has worked extremely closely with a wide range of carefully selected suppliers in a partnership approach to the design and build process and we are particularly grateful to the teams from STX Europe who have constructed two world class ships in their impressive yards at Rauma in Finland. The two vessels are not the cheapest we could have bought but I firmly believe they are the best, and the quality of the overall fit and finish is second to none.

The naval architects at DeltaMarin and STX have produced for us a unique and highly fuel efficient hull form that will make these ships the most efficient cross-Channel ferries of all time. And we are particularly pleased with the excellent advice we have received from SMC and others in terms of the modern and comfortable internal design.

In the ferry industry, wise heads talk of never being able to beat a ship that is purpose built for a route. And here I firmly believe that we have raised the bar again in the long tradition of our company's leadership in innovation and customer service on the Channel.

But as we proudly welcome the new, we should pay tribute to the old. The ships we are replacing, the *Pride of Dover* and *Pride of Calais*, have done us proud over their combined service totalling almost 50 years.

Between them they have given indefatigable service and have carried many millions of passengers, millions of vehicles and many more millions of tons of freight. They have played a crucial role in the UK's logistic supply chain and we salute them both.

When they were introduced they were hailed as revolutionary due to their size, with double the carrying capacity of the previous generation of ferries.

With *Spirit of Britain* and *Spirit of France* we have doubled the carrying capacity yet again and these will be the largest ferries capable of operating in the existing ferry berths of Dover and Calais. They innovate in many other ways, too, and this book is dedicated to explaining how and why.

The dawn of one new era in cross-Channel ferry transport and travel is upon us.

Contents

Produced and designed by Ferry Publications trading as Lily Publications Ltd
PO Box 33, Ramsey, Isle of Man, British Isles, IM99 4LP
Tel: +44 (0) 1624 898446   Fax: +44 (0) 1624 898449
www.ferrypubs.co.uk   E-Mail: info@lilypublications.co.uk
Printed and bound by Gomer Press Ltd., Wales, UK +44 (0) 1559 362371 © Lily Publications 2011
Published: March 2011

chapter
one

Introduction

Many fine examples of cross-Channel ferries have been produced during the recent history of the service, the most important of which are those which are regarded as the trendsetters or reference ships in terms of mechanical innovation, passenger facilities or simply in matters of size and capacity.

The ferry industry has certainly come a long way from the days of this writer's childhood when cars were lifted on and off by crane at Dover's Admiralty Pier. The introduction of drive on – drive off at Dover's Eastern Docks in 1953 was a tremendous advance but the early vehicle ferries catered for tourist cars and the industry therefore remained seasonal in nature.

During the 1960s, the advent of multi-purpose vessels carrying lorries, cars and passengers required ships of higher vehicle deck headroom of drive-through design as reversing lorries on board was a slow and arduous process. As the industry grew, twin vehicle-decked ferries were introduced and yet prior to the ending of duty-free allowances, these ships also provided ample capacity for large numbers of foot passengers.

'CHUNNEL BEATERS'

At Dover, the 1980s saw both the nationalised British Rail and partners SNCF (trading as Sealink) and Townsend Thoresen fleets each introduce a trio of new ferries which increased competition to new heights. For the first time, capacity was greatly enlarged with the ferries boasting two drive-through lorry decks. Then, during 1987, in anticipation of the opening of the Channel Tunnel, P&O European Ferries (successors to Townsend Thoresen) took the new concept a stage further by unveiling their 'Chunnel Beaters', the *Pride of Dover* and *Pride of Calais*.

Ever since they entered service, these ships set the standard on the Dover Strait. Their design was shaped by the knowledge that they would need to compete with the Channel Tunnel and encapsulated their owners' response to the changing trends in the short-sea market. The company had always sought to optimise new ship designs around discernable patterns of traffic, never basing their entire design planning around a single type. With the introduction of the sisters they had simply responded to trends without unduly affecting operational flexibility in terms of carrying capacity.

The *Spirit of Free Enterprise* class of ships (of 1980) had been developed at a time when hovercraft operation was in its ascendancy. It was seen as important to attract and win back holiday traffic while boosting the blossoming day excursion market. Just seven years later, the new *Pride of Dover* class were indicative of the continued growth in vehicle traffic and the continuing improvements in the day-trip trade.

Never before, within such a short period of time, had purpose-built ships constructed for the same company to operate on the same route differed so widely in their size and specification. The

Entering service in December 1987, the *Pride of Calais* will be replaced in the fleet by the *Spirit of France*. She is seen when new and in the days before enclosed bridge wings. *(FotoFlite)*

increase in car space was 90%, in passenger capacity 73% while freight capacity was doubled. Their commercial aim was simply to upgrade the experience of travelling which was immediately evident to all those who used the ships. Their vast size coupled with the range, variety and number of retail outlets was a bold and positive statement on behalf of the ferry industry.

During their 1991-92 refits, both 1987 sisters received extensive £3 million upgrades of their passenger facilities. The installation of Club Class had occurred during their previous overhauls and this

had proved to be an immediate success. The brand name of P&O has always been synonymous with cruise-style comfort and the reintroduction of First Class travel across the Dover Strait was long overdue. No longer was a cross-Channel voyage something to be endured but it was now an experience to be enjoyed. The new ships, and those that followed, very much continued to express P&O's approach to cross-Channel travel and once all the work had been completed, Managing Director Graeme Dunlop was able to speak of "the recent revolution in standards of service".

This illuminating illustration shows the actual size of the new ferries against the *Pride of Dover* and *Pride of Calais* class of 1987. *(P&O Ferries)*

Introduction

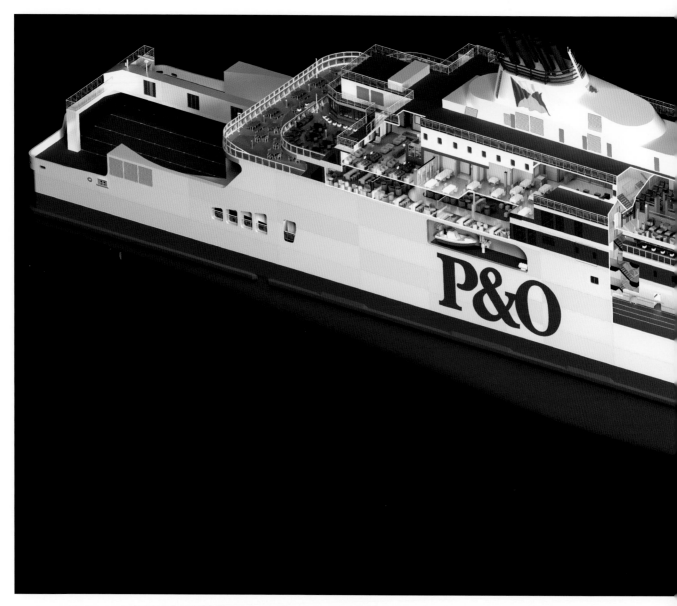

This cutaway illustration shows the principal passenger areas on Decks 8 and 9. *(P&O Ferries)*

Much has happened since the *Pride of Dover* and *Pride of Calais* entered service and the Channel Tunnel now takes about half of the cross-Channel traffic on offer. Duty-free concessions have ended and consequently the day-trip market (mainly foot passengers) has seriously contracted. Competition remains but the hovercraft and other fast catamarans have come and gone. Escalating fuel prices, premium fares and limited on-board facilities weighed against a saving in time of perhaps 20 minutes on a calm day all conspired to remove the fast craft concept from the short-sea routes.

P&O CHANGES

The volatile nature of the ferry industry has also witnessed other changes. In recent years, the P&O Group has fragmented with P&O Princess Cruises being acquired by the Carnival Corporation in 2003 and the ports and ferries division being swallowed up by Dubai Ports World in March 2006 in a deal worth some £3.9 billion. Their acquisition of P&O Ferries finally allowed the company to consider the building of new tonnage and the lengthy process commenced of drawing up specifications for an entirely new and innovative class of cross-Channel ferry. What has been achieved is as epoch-making as the *Pride of Dover* class; the twin ships completely outweigh, outshine and outclass their competitors and become by far the largest ferries to ever operate across the English Channel.

Following the detailed and lengthy evaluation processes, the £330

million order for yard numbers 1367 and 1368 was made on 7th August 2008. A number of ship builders were consulted in Italy, South Korea, Croatia and Finland but the undertaking of an earlier delivery and a quality premium paid to build in Europe proved to be the deciding factors.

The building contract was finally awarded to Aker at Rauma in Finland. Within months, the chosen yard had become STX Europe to reflect the entry of the South Korean-based STX Business Group as principal shareholder in the company during summer 2008.

UNIQUE

When building new ships, due to simple matters of economics, many ferry operators turn to a yard and opt for a standard design package with standard fittings sourced from a limited number of contractors. What was unusual in this present build process was that P&O Ferries were able to present their own advanced plans to Aker/STX for a unique pair of ships. It has been seen on many occasions that if ferries are to be successful on any route, they must be custom built to serve it. The Dover-Calais operation is so specialist and intensive with short crossing times and quick turn-rounds in port that a standard shipyard design simply would not suffice. If there is any route around the British Isles that demands specialist ships then it is undoubtedly Dover-Calais.

At Channel House, Dover, the final Phase 6 drawings were duly

Introduction

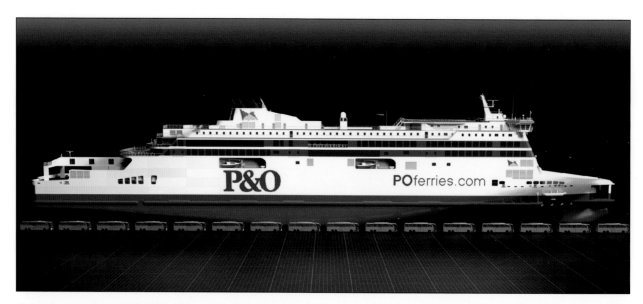

It's only by comparing something with which we are familiar in everyday life with the new ships that we are able to gain a real impression of their size. The vehicle decks can accommodate 3.5 kilometres of traffic. *(P&O Ferries)*

approved at the end of February 2009 ready for the first steel for yard number 1367 to be cut in March. With the keel duly laid on 25th August, construction using the latest prefabricated methods proceeded at pace. In spite of the coldest Scandinavian winter for 20 years, on 8th June 2010 the first ship was floated out of her dry dock. Fitting out was followed by trials before on 5th January 2011, she left Finland for Dover where she arrived four days later.

It had originally been P&O's intention to name the new ferries *Olympic Spirit* and *Olympic Pride* but it was later agreed to modify

the names to the more traditional *Spirit of Britain* and *Spirit of France*. These trendsetting ships pioneer an entirely new generation of cross-Channel ferry. Not so very long ago it was unthinkable that ships of this size would ever be introduced on the premier link with the Continent. That P&O have made this considerable commitment and are championing this huge advance in ship design is surely a bold statement in their belief that the second decade of the 21st century is truly the age of the ferry.

The *Spirit of Britain* afloat at last and awaiting her tugs on 9th June 2010. *(John Hendy)*

The *Spirit of Britain* in the Gulf of Bothnia on her first day of trials on 23rd November 2010. Released from the confines of the shipyard, the ship is at last viewed in her element. *(STX Europe)*

This three-quarter stern view of the *Spirit of Britain* shows her clean and simple lines to advantage. *(FotoFlite)*

chapter
two

P&O
Ferries

THE P&O STORY

Although P&O Ferries is a relative newcomer to the world of shipping, the origins of the Peninsular and Oriental Steam Navigation Company can be traced as far back as 1815.

By 1823 the firm was known as Willcox and Anderson, and the business had expanded to include the operation of small sailing vessels to Spain and Portugal, as agents for the owners. In the early 1830s the partners began to charter steamers, soon adopting the trading name Peninsular Steam Navigation Company and the company's first owned ship, the newly built *Iberia*, entered service on the route to Spain and Portugal.

The partners had raised loans, chartered steamers for use as troopships and warships, and engaged in gun running for the Royal Houses in both the Spanish and Portuguese Civil Wars in the early 1830s and as a result, were granted the right to fly both sets of Royal colours. The famous P&O house flag showing the red and yellow of Spain and the blue and white of Portugal, is still proudly worn today by the ships of P&O Ferries.

By 1971, the activities of more than 100 subsidiary companies were amalgamated into operating divisions within P&O. All of the cargo ships formerly operated by P&O and its subsidiaries were put into the General Cargo Division, the liners, along with British India's educational cruise ships formed the Passenger Division, and the tankers, bulk carriers and gas carriers became the fleet of the Bulk Shipping Division. From this time the ships of constituent companies flew the P&O flag and began to adopt a corporate identity. Following this reorganisation, the fleet consisted of 239 ships, including 136 general cargo liners, 27 coasters, 18 passenger liners, 17 ferries, 17 tankers and 6 bulk carriers.

The 1970s were years of diversification away from shipping. A large network of road haulage operations was built up under the Ferrymasters, Pandoro, P&O Roadways and P&O Roadtanks names and construction group Bovis was acquired in 1974. By March 1999, the Group, including joint ventures and associates, was again a major force to be reckoned with in the shipping world, controlling some 276 ships.

At the same time P&O's Chairman announced that it was his Board's intention to refocus the Group on the three core businesses: cruising, ferries, and ports and logistics. Disposal of property and service company interests began and by early October almost £1 billion had been realised from the sale of investment properties, Bovis Construction, Laing (Canada), service companies in Australia, and the London exhibition halls of Earls Court and Olympia.

It was known that P&O was prepared to move out of the container trades by floating P&O Nedlloyd on the stock-market but the announcement in February 2000 that the Company would rid itself of its cruise business was a total surprise.

On 23rd October 2000, P&O Princess Cruises de-merged from the Peninsular and Oriental Steam Navigation Company (P&O) to become an independent trading company. Then, during April 2003 the Miami-based Carnival Corporation merged with P&O Princess Cruises to form Carnival Corporation & plc, the world's largest cruise company.

Although former Prime Minister Mrs Margaret Thatcher is quoted as saying of P&O: "It's not just a company but the very fabric of the Empire," the company's 168 years of independence was coming to an end and following a period of uncertainty, on 29th November 2005 they announced that Dubai Ports (DP World) had taken them over in a deal worth £3.3 billion. P&O stated that it was not actively looking for a takeover bid but the offer proved too attractive to resist and shareholders agreed to the takeover on 13th February 2006. DP World was one of several Dubai Government-linked firms looking for assets to invest in, backed by huge cash piles from the Gulf emirate's resources. Compared with the ports division, which was the principal prize that DP World was interested in adding to its portfolio, P&O Ferries proved to be very small in terms of the total package that the Dubai-based company acquired and was really outside their area of expertise or even interest. After a period of uncertainty during which time the future direction of the ferry company was in doubt, the new owners were able to allay fears when they announced that P&O Ferries was not for sale.

Thus P&O Ferries continues to be managed and operated from its Channel House Headquarters at Dover, high on a hill above the town and overlooking both the harbour and the Dover Strait.

A crane loading the *Forde* in The Camber at Dover in 1930 as anxious motorists look on. Although she was fitted with a stern gate, it was only used once at Calais during the French General Strike in June 1936. *(Ferry Publications Library)*

TOWNSEND AND P&O FERRIES (DOVER)

The ancestry of the P&O involvement at Dover goes back to 1928 when Mr Stuart M. Townsend chartered the 368-ton collier *Artificer* for a brief summer season to offer motorists a cut-price motor car ferry service linking Dover with Calais. Townsend's original plan was to end the monopoly then enjoyed by the Southern Railway Company, undercut their fares by half and force them to reduce their rates after which he would withdraw. His initial success saw a

The scene at Dover Eastern Docks shortly after the arrival of the revolutionary *Free Enterprise* from her Dutch builders in 1962. British Railway's turbine steamers *Maid of Kent* (left) and *Lord Warden* occupy the port's twin berths. *(Captain JE Dawson's collection)*

P&O Ferries

profit of £80 in the first season which prompted a further charter during 1929 after which the former minesweeper HMS *Ford* was purchased and converted for merchant use after being inspected at the scrap yard at Dover's Eastern Docks.

Renamed *Forde*, the 11-year-old steamer commenced her seasonal service in April 1930 carrying up to 168 passengers and 28 cars. She was an immediate success and throughout the thirties the family-owned 'Townsend Channel Ferry' blossomed.

Townsend had seen from an early time that the drive-on method of loading was the way ahead but the authorities on both sides of the Channel were reluctant to allow the construction of linkspans over which cars could be driven between ship and shore. The *Forde* was actually rebuilt with a stern gate and when in June 1936 a French General Strike paralysed the cranes at Calais, at high water she simply presented her stern to the quay and allowed her vehicles to drive directly onto French soil. All those who witnessed this historic occasion saw the foundations laid for a transport revolution.

Success continued after the war and the elderly *Forde* was sold for further service at Gibraltar. Her replacement was another former Royal Navy vessel, the 'River' class frigate HMS *Halladale*. After her conversion at Cork, she took up service in April 1950 and in the following June opened the drive-on ramp at Calais although she was not able to use similar facilities at Dover until April 1953.

In 1956, continued growth prompted Townsend to go public but the share issue was launched on the very day that President Nasser announced the nationalisation of the Suez Canal. Trade on the Stock Exchange slumped and few shares were sold.

At this time the Coventry-based Mr George Nott and his associates were scouring the market looking for a small company with large assets which they could transfer to their own. A controlling interest in Townsend Bros. Car Ferries was duly secured after which the Townsend family's involvement eventually ceased. It was initially Nott's intention to strip the ferry company of its assets and to wind-up the ferry service but sense prevailed and the *Halladale* continued to make handsome profits for her new owners.

The new regime was far more aggressive and now looked further afield than the traditionally seasonal car ferry traffic. Some of its ideas were very forward-looking and were amply illustrated when in 1959 a subsidiary company European Ferries was formed and the former tank-landing craft *Empire Shearwater* was taken on long-term charter to provide a service for lorries and heavy vehicles. Sadly the climate was not then right for such a link and after just six months it ended in failure.

The first of the well-known green-hulled ferries, the £1 million *Free Enterprise* entered service in April 1962 and was followed in May 1965 by the *Free Enterprise II* – the first British-registered drive-through ferry. She opened the Dover-Zeebrugge link in March 1966 after which time, expansion – especially of freight – was tremendous and between 1966 and 1974 six more larger 'Free Enterprise' vessels were added to the fleet.

The year 1968 had seen the acquisition of the Norwegian-owned Thoresen Car Ferries after which the European Ferries Group was created and eventually the combined fleets adopted the orange hulls of the Thoresen ships. The enlarged company was the largest independent ferry concern in Europe and was further strengthened in 1971 by the purchase of the Atlantic Steam Navigation Company and in 1985 of the Dover-Boulogne operators P&O Normandy Ferries and their three small ships *Lion*, *nf Tiger* and *nf Panther*.

The continuing demand for freight space particularly on the Zeebrugge link saw the introduction of three 'European' class roll on – roll off freighters in 1975, 1976 and 1978. The *Free Enterprise VI* and *Free Enterprise VII* both underwent major surgery in 1985 when they were raised and lengthened to increase their lorry capacity from 24 to 60 units. The result was not a pretty sight but this clever piece of engineering allowed two well-tried ships to continue their successful careers at a time when the cost of building replacements would have been prohibitive.

Some five years earlier the company had introduced a completely new generation of cross-Channel ferries. The *Spirit of Free Enterprise* and her two sisters offered 75-minute crossings which enabled as many as five daily round sailings to be operated between Dover and Calais by each ship. They were the first Channel ferries to be built with twin vehicle decks both capable of carrying freight. Such was the success of the concept that when plans for the present fixed cross-Channel link were unveiled, Townsend Thoresen soon declared their intention of offering their own 'Channel Beaters' – twin giant ferries (with double the lorry capacity of the previous 'Spirit' class) which they claimed would threaten the financial viability of the tunnel.

The £85 million *Pride of Dover* and *Pride of Calais* both entered service during 1987 but prior to this (in January 1986) the P&O Group had acquired a controlling interest in a company holding almost 21% of the European Ferries Group shares. P&O Chairman Sir Jeffrey Sterling was invited to join the Board and from that time the future of the EFG was always in doubt. By this time the company

The *Free Enterprise II* of 1965 was the first UK registered drive-through ferry. *(FotoFlite)*

The *Pride of Calais* and *Pride of Dover* are seen passing each other off Calais. Trendsetters in their time, they are now surpassed by the latest generation of Channel ferry. *(FotoFlite)*

had accrued large land holdings in the United States where a drop in oil prices eventually brought the EFG to its knees. The Board invited P&O to act as their life raft and this was duly accomplished in January 1987. The ferry division continued to trade as Townsend Thoresen but following the 'Herald' disaster off Zeebrugge in March, P&O acted decisively to distance themselves from the former regime and duly created P&O European Ferries in October 1987.

During 1991-93, four more vessels were added to the Dover-based fleet in the form of the three 'Super-European' class freighters for the Zeebrugge link and their half sister the *Pride of Burgundy* which entered service in April 1993. With the stretching of the *Pride of Kent* (formerly the *Spirit of Free Enterprise*) in June 1992, the P&O European Ferries fleet of super ferries now numbered five. The fitting of Club Class and luxury lounges on all ships set a standard which was the envy of others and the company carried three times more traffic from Dover and Calais than their nearest competitor.

During the preparation for the opening of the tunnel, the secondary passenger routes to Zeebrugge (in December 1991) and Boulogne (in January 1993) were closed although Zeebrugge continued in a freight-only capacity until December 2002. It was important that all efforts should be directed at the premier route against the tunnel and so services that weakened that position were terminated. As it was, P&O European Ferries had its own Channel Shuttle service up and running by summer 1993 a whole year and a half before the tunnel eventually opened.

P&O STENA LINE

During July 1996 the Department of Trade and Industry gave both P&O European Ferries and Stena Line UK Ltd the 'amber' light allowing them to adopt some form of co-operation in response to the Channel Tunnel. A Memorandum of Understanding was signed that October when it was agreed that both companies would supply 14 vessels (8 from P&OEF and 5 from Stena in addition to a fast craft) for the Dover-Zeebrugge, Dover-Calais and Newhaven-Dieppe routes. After further delays, Government permission for the 'Joint Venture' was given in November 1997 and the new company was officially launched on 9th March 1998. The vessels concerned were as follows:

Pride of Dover - P&OSL Dover
Pride of Calais - P&OSL Calais
Pride of Bruges (I)- P&OSL Picardy but withdrawn February 2000
Pride of Burgundy - P&OSL Burgundy
Pride of Kent - P&OSL Kent
European Seaway
European Pathway
European Highway
Stena Empereur - P&OSL Provence
Stena Fantasia - P&OSL Canterbury
Stena Invicta - chartered and renamed *Color Viking*
Stena Cambria - withdrawn in January 1999
Stena Antrim - withdrawn in March 1998

A joint venture between P&O Ferries and Stena Line operated between 1998 and 2002 before the Swedish company withdrew from the arrangement. The unsuccessful **P&OSL Provence** (later **Pride of Provence**) was part of the Swedish input into the joint service. *(FotoFlite)*

Elite (fast craft) - handed back to Stena in October 1998

The original plan was for the *Pride of Bruges* to be switched to the Newhaven-Dieppe service and trials were duly made. However, the *Stena Antrim* was withdrawn and sold and sister vessel *Stena Cambria,* with her more modern interior, was placed on the link to operate with the fast craft, *Elite* (formerly the *Stena Lynx III*). The 'Invicta' was immediately dispensed with, as with only one freight deck her use would be limited on the Calais link and so she never operated for the new company. The Dieppe link continued to lose money and the *Elite* was withdrawn from service as being unreliable and prone to delays or cancellations in bad weather. P&O Stena Line eventually closed the link on 31st January 1999 after which the French crews from the *Stena Cambria* were switched to the Zeebrugge freighter *European Pathway*.

At the time, this vessel was enduring a prolonged period off service with a broken gearbox and finding themselves a ship short for the Zeebrugge link duly chartered the *Stena Royal* which had been laid up at Dunkirk since the closure of RMT's Ostend-Ramsgate link in February 1997. As the *Prins Filip*, the former flagship of the Belgian Government's fleet, this vessel represented that concern's last effort to save the ailing link. She was a splendid vessel which had entered service in 1992 and was built with the finest materials that the Belgian taxpayer could afford. One of Stena's numerous companies had purchased the idle vessel in June 1998 and this was her first service since the Ostend link had closed.

Although much mechanical work was required, it was soon realised that the *Stena Royal* was too good a ship to lose and her charter was duly extended (with an option to purchase) at which time she was renamed *P&OSL Aquitaine*. After a major internal and mechanical refit, the ship took up sailings to Calais during November 1999 replacing the smaller *P&OSL Picardy* in the fleet. After a brief lay-up at Dunkirk, the latter vessel was duly sold to TransEuropa Ferries and today operates as the *Oleander* on that company's Ostend-Ramsgate link.

The Stena side of the partnership held a 40% stake in the joint-venture company. Stena Line of Gothenburg in Sweden took over the former Sealink fleet following a hostile takeover battle with Sea Containers in April 1990. Sealink had been de-nationalised and sold for just £66 million in July 1984 after which the company traded as Sealink British Ferries. No purpose-built tonnage was added to any route apart from those to the Isle of Wight (which Sea Containers retained in 1990) but Stena's purchase of the company for £259 million severely stretched the Swedes and amongst the early casualties was the historic Folkestone-Boulogne link.

While Townsend Thoresen and then P&O European Ferries were constructing new super ferries and upgrading their service, Sealink Stena Line continued to run with converted and second-hand vessels introducing the *Fantasia* in 1990 followed by the *Stena Invicta* with the ro-pax ferry *Stena Challenger* in 1991. After an £8 million refit the *Stena Empereur* (ex *Stena Jutlandica*) joined the

The *Pride of Calais* as she appeared towards the end of her career in the Dover Strait with enclosed bridge wings (fitted in 2004) and the later application of the company livery with the blue hull paint lowered. *(John Hendy)*

Calais service in July 1996 after which the 'Challenger' sailed to the Holyhead station.

The Sealink and then Stena operation at Dover was always run as a joint venture with French partners Sealink SNAT but due to increased friction between them, this ceased at the end of 1995 when the French floated their own company known as SeaFrance. It is of interest that this is still marketed as 'Sealink' across the Channel.

Stena Line operated all three of its smaller fast craft at various times, the last to be used being the 74-metre *Stena Lynx* during winter 1997/98, and the *Stena Cambria* (formerly the *St. Anselm*)

The *Pride of Kent* was the result of a successful freight ship conversion in 2003. *(John Hendy)*

also provided extra tonnage after the Stena/SNCF split but the fleet was an odd mixture of vessels catering for a specific end of the market (quite different to that offered by P&O) with their Travel Service Concept. Much work was completed to bring the former Stena ships up to P&O standards with the *Pride of Provence* (ex *Stena Empereur*) coming in for particular attention.

The P&O Stena Line joint venture duly ended during autumn 2002 when P&O purchased Stena's share of the business for £150 million. Following this, all name prefixes reverted to 'Pride of' rather than 'P&OSL' although for a brief period this was modified to just 'PO'. At the same time P&O North Sea Ferries and P&O Portsmouth merged with the now 100% P&O-owned P&O Stena Line to become simply P&O Ferries.

P&O FERRIES

Although in 2001, car traffic was again taken on the Zeebrugge link, a decision to convert the sisters *European Pathway* and *European Highway* to dual-purpose mode for the Dover-Calais service saw the service end on 15th December 2002. Both ships were sent to Bremerhaven for conversion and were renamed *Pride of Canterbury* (II) and *Pride of Kent* (II) in a double naming ceremony at Dover's Admiralty Pier. They replaced the earlier ships with those names, the former Stena ship *PO Canterbury* (ex *Fantasia*) and *PO Kent* (ex *Pride of Kent*) which were both sold to Greek owners GA Ferries although after a single season in the Mediterranean, the

P&O Ferries

A useful comparison in size and scale between the *Pride of Bruges* (of 1980) and the *Pride of Burgundy* (of 1992). *(John Hendy)*

former *Fantasia* was resold to Polish operators Polferries. The last member of the eclectic former Stena fleet, the *Pride of Provence* (ex *Stena Empereur*) was also sold to GA Ferries in 2004 but was quickly passed on to the Norwegian company Kystlink for service between Norway and Denmark.

With the closure of the Zeebrugge service, the remaining freighter *European Seaway* was switched to the Calais route but serious financial problems followed by a thorough re-evaluation and reorganisation of the fleet in 2004 saw the ship laid up in Birkenhead and offered for sale during which time the *Pride of Burgundy* operated in a freight-only mode. However, in the following year it was decided to recall the 'Seaway' and lay up the more

expensive to operate vessel *Pride of Aquitaine* which was on charter from one of the many Stena Line subsidiaries and which was duly passed on to the French LD Lines for the Portsmouth-Le Havre link.

There had been much discussion in recent years concerning new tonnage for the Calais service and an order was finally made in June 2008 for twin 49,000 gross ton Finnish-built sister ships for entry into service during January and September 2011. With space for more than 170 lorries (or 800 cars) and facilities for up to 2,000 passengers, these latest trendsetting ships set completely new standards on the English Channel.

Eighty years of vehicle ferry growth						
Year	Ferry	Gross tonnage	Length (metres)	Passengers	Cars	Lorries
1930	*Forde*	710	69.3	168	28	
1952	*Halladale*	1,370	90.5	350	55	
1962	*Free Enterprise*	2,607	96.5	846	120	
1965	*Free Enterprise II*	4,122	108	1,000	205	
1974	*Free Enterprise VIII*	4,981	117.5	1,132	314	24
1980	*Spirit of Free Enterprise*	7,951	132.5	1,300	350	50
1987	*Pride of Dover*	26,433	169.6	2,290	650	85
1993	*Pride of Burgundy*	28,138	179.7	1,420	600	120
2003	*Pride of Canterbury*	30,365	179.7	2,000	650	120
2011	*Spirit of Britain*	47,592	213	2,000	1,000	170+

DOVER-CALAIS FERRY TIME LINE

1904   The *Onward* carries the first car across the Channel from Folkestone to Boulogne.

1911   The *Engadine* and *Riviera* are built with strengthened decks for the carriage of motor cars.

1928   Stuart Townsend charters the collier *Artificer* (15 cars, 12 passengers) for a month.

1930   Townsend introduces the converted minesweeper *Forde* (28 cars, 168 passengers) into service between Dover and Calais.

1936   The Dover-Dunkirk train ferry commences allowing cars to be driven on at the side.

1950   Townsend introduces the converted frigate *Halladale* (55 cars, 350 passengers).

1951   Calais Chamber of Commerce opens the new car ferry linkspan at berth 3.

1952   British Railways introduce the *Lord Warden*, the first purpose-built car ferry for the Dover Strait.

1953   Dover Harbour Board opens the Eastern Docks Car Ferry Terminal.

1962   Townsend introduce the *Free Enterprise* (120 cars, 846 passengers).

1965   The *Free Enterprise II* becomes the UK's first drive-through car ferry.

1968   Townsend absorb Southampton-based Thoresen Car Ferries to form the European Ferries Group.

1971   The European Ferries Group take over the Atlantic Steam Navigation Company's Transport Ferry Service.

1974   The eighth and final vessel of the 'Free Enterprise' class (FE VIII) enters service.

1980   The *Spirit of Free Enterprise* enters service and offers twin, drive-through lorry decks.

1985   The European Ferries Group take over P&O Normandy Ferries (Boulogne and Le Havre routes).

1986   P&O take over the European Ferries Group (Townsend Thoresen).

1987   The 'Chunnel Beaters' *Pride of Dover* and *Pride of Calais* enter service.

P&O European Ferries is formed in October.

1993   The *Pride of Burgundy* enters service.

2003   Two former Zeebrugge freight vessels (of 1991) are completely rebuilt and reappear as the *Pride of Canterbury* and *Pride of Kent*.

2011   The *Spirit of Britain* and *Spirit of France* become the largest Dover-Calais ferries yet.

Townsend's ***Forde*** leaving Dover in 1948. *(Ferry Publications Library)*

Townsend's ***Free Enterprise*** crossing the Dover Strait in her inaugural 1962 season. *(FotoFlite)*

The ***Pride of Bruges*** was the third of the ***Spirit of Free Enterprise*** trio of 1980. *(John Hendy)*

The 'Chunnel Beater' ***Pride of Calais*** entered service in 1987. *(John Hendy)*

chapter
three

Building the Spirit of Britain at STX Europe

Right: August 2009 and the first building block is laid in the STX dry dock at Rauma. *(Brian Smith)*

Top left: The scale of the ship's building blocks can be gained by comparison with the shipyard workers below. *(Brian D. Smith)*

Left: Left to right, Steve Morant, Mike Langley, John Garner and Helen Deeble at the keel laying ceremony. *(Brian D. Smith)*

Above: John Garner and Helen Deeble with their lucky coins ready to place in position on the ship's keel block.*(Brian D. Smith)*

Top left: By October 2009, the ship was already starting to take shape with machinery already placed in Decks 1 and 2. *(Brian D. Smith)*

Left: Part of the main vehicle deck (Deck 3) has been added to the hull. *(STX Europe)*

Top view: Another view of the first Deck 3 modules in position. *(Brian D. Smith)*

Above centre: On board the ship showing the work on Deck 3. *(Brian D. Smith)*

Above: Part of the bow section showing the apertures for the three bow-thrust units is lowered into position. *(Brian D. Smith)*

Top: The bulbous bow and Deck 3's forward extension are ready for fitting. Notice that the Calais port-fit 'spade' is asymmetrical. This is due to the fact that the ship's bow is too wide to fit the berths and is therefore offset. (Brian D. Smith)

Left: One of the staircases connecting the passenger areas on Decks 8 and 9 with the vehicle decks. (Brian D. Smith)

Above: Below the bridge, the door to Deck 5 opens onto the upper freight deck.(Brian D. Smith)

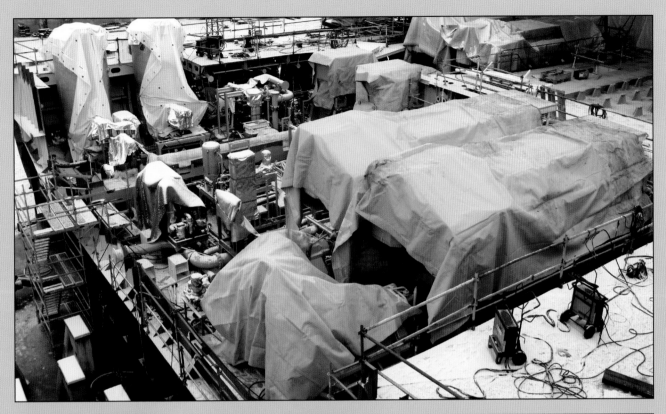

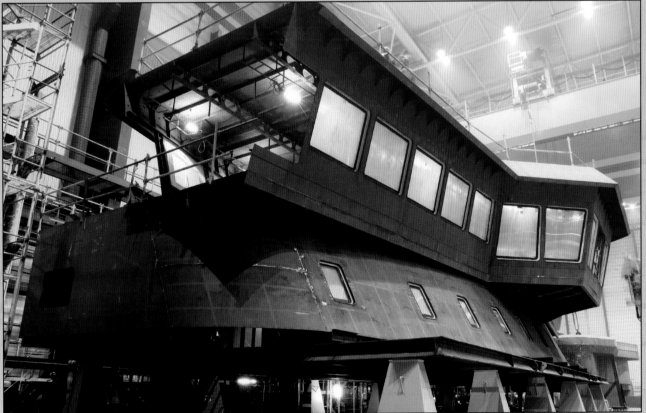

Top : This December 2009 picture shows two of the ship's four main engines in position and protected against the winter snow. *(Brian D. Smith)*

Above: In the STX construction hall, the *Spirit of Britain*'s bridge section is ready for outshipping. *(STX Europe)*

Right: By December 2009, the ship's main staircases were starting to take shape. (Brian Smith)

Left: Another accommodation section is meticulously lowered into position. (Brian D. Smith)

Above: The main freight deck on Deck 3 with the ship's central casing on the left. (Brian D. Smith)

Top: More passenger modules are lowered into position during December 2009. *(Brian D. Smith)*

Bottom Left: The entrances to all three vehicle decks are seen in this December 2009 image.*(Brian D. Smith)*

Above: Work in progress on Deck 7 - the car deck. *(Brian D. Smith)*

In December 2009, the forward end of the ship was looking recognisable but much work was still required to her after end. The sub-zero temperatures made life extremely difficult for the STX men. *(Brian D. Smith)*

Top: Fighting against the weather at Rauma as piles of snow accumulate in the bottom of the dry dock. *(Brian D. Smith)*

Left middle: Deck 5 covered in ice with Deck 7 above. Note the difference in headroom.*(Brian D. Smith)*

Left: Work progresses in the Food Court. *(Brian Smith)*

Above: A bow view with the water tight doors in Deck 3 already in position. *(Brian D. Smith)*

Top: You really can see the join between building blocks in this photograph of the vessel's bow! This view illustrates the Calais port fit: both bow and stern doors are wider than necessary due to the berth limitations on both sides of the Channel. *(Brian D. Smith)*

Left: Looking down at the bow with the bridge superstructure on the dock side ready to be craned aboard. *(Brian D. Smith)*

Above: Work continues behind the bridge on the helipad area. *(Brian D. Smith)*

In March 2010, the bridge section is finally lifted into position. Note the twin windows in the floor of the bridge wing which allow the Master to see the quayside during the docking procedure. *(Brian D. Smith)*

6th June 2010 Float Out

Right: With the open sea dead astern, the *Spirit of Britain* is viewed from her monkey-island prior to her float out on a glorious June summer's day. *(John Hendy)*

Top left: An early view of Routemasters' - the facilities dedicated to lorry drivers on Deck 9. *(John Hendy)*

Left: The Food Court's panoramic windows were already flooding light into the ship. *(John Hendy)*

Above: The Family Lounge on Deck 8 with metres of coiled cable hanging from the deckhead. *(Miles Cowsill)*

Top: The ship's twin four-bladed propellers and rudders. *(John Hendy)*

Left: The *Spirit of Britain* is seen from the dock side with the *Spirit of France*'s first building block on the left. *(John Hendy)*

Above: One of the three bow-thrust propellers in position prior to the float out. *(John Hendy)*

Top and centre left: The dry dock's five valves are simultaneously opened allowing the sea to cascade in. The playing of the local brass band and the release of balloons added to the happy occasion. *(John Hendy)*

Left: The official keel laying ceremony of the *Spirit of France* also took place on 6th June 2010. Representatives of the shipyard, the MCA and Lloyd's along with P&O's Project Team. (Left to Right) Vince Todd, Mike Langley, Steve Morant, Steve Parkhsuø, Heikki Tuomikoski (Delta Marine) and Nick Blyth. *(John Hendy)*

Above: (Left to Right), Chief Engineer Steve Stagg, Chris Henson, John Garner, Robert Woods (Chairman, P&O Ferries), Helen Deeble, Simon Johnson, Mike O'Dwyer, Captain David Miller and Nigel Davies. *(Miles Cowsill)*

Top: The water lapping against the ship's keel blocks. This image shows her revolutionary underwater design and also her port stabiliser fin in its hull housing. *(John Hendy)*

Left: The *Spirit of Britain* towers above the quayside at Rauma as she waits to be floated out of her dry dock. *(John Hendy)*

Top: Afloat at last as the late afternoon sun swings around to illuminate the ship's port side. Note the building blocks for the *Spirit of France* on the left of this view. The construction sheds are in the far distance. *(Miles Cowsill)*

Below: Company at last! The tug *Harald* was one of three such vessels that nursed the *Spirit of Britain* to her fitting out berth. Her individual building blocks are very evident. *(John Hendy)*

Top: Moving the 'dead' ship out of the dry dock towards the fitting out quay was a slow and laborious task. *(John Hendy)*

Left: Once clear of the dock, the ship was swung in order to be starboard side to the fitting out berth. By the time that this task was completed, the sun had set on a glorious day. *(John Hendy)*

Top: October 2010 and the *Spirit of Britain* was receiving the final touches to her paintwork as she glistens in the late autumn sunshine. *(Brian D. Smith)*

Centre left: Deck 5 and (Bottom left) Deck 3 await their first vehicles. *(Brian D. Smith)*

Above: Trials of the ship's ability to accommodate cars and caravans via the ramps to Deck 7 were successful. *(Brian D. Smith)*

Top left: Fitting out the Club Lounge. *(Brian D. Smith)*

Left: The port side bridge overhang and its floor 'windows' to assist when docking. *(Brian D. Smith)*

Above: Work continues on the (top) Family Lounge, (centre) Food Court and (below) Brasserie. *(All Brian D. Smith))*

Almost ready for trials. *(Brian D. Smith)*

P&O

TUG

Spirit of Britain
IMO 9524231

Top: On 23rd November, the *Spirit of Britain* left Rauma for four days of official trials in the Gulf of Bothnia. *(STX Europe)*

Left: The ship's white funnel with a broad blue band is a new departure for P&O Ferries. *(Brian D. Smith)*

Above: A pilot's view of the ship's helipad which is sited behind the bridge. *(Brian D. Smith)*

chapter four

The
ferries of the
future

THE 2006 RO-RO CONFERENCE

During May 2006 Mike Langley, Programme Manager for the new P&O Ferries, attended the Ro-Ro Conference in Ghent. A key presentation was given by BC Ferries and the Flensburg shipyard concerning the three 'Celebration' class double-ended ferries which the German yard was building to augment the ferry services to Vancouver Island in Canada.

At an earlier period in time, P&O had seriously considered providing a double-ended ferry for the Dover-Calais link and there is little doubt that in certain respects such a ship would have been advantageous. At Dover, ferries have to swing and run astern to present their after ends to the linkspans while at Calais, although on arrival they can simply manoeuvre their bows into the linkspan cradle, on departure a 180-degree swing is required in order to point the bow back in the direction of Dover. This invariably means that time is wasted at both ports in manoeuvring and particularly at Calais. A double-ended ship design, of which the Canadian operators BC Ferries have a number of examples, would have eliminated these problems. However, there are also disadvantages with this type of vessel which are largely based on matters of space and cost. A large double-ended ferry requires two bridges with a doubling up of everything electrical and technological at both ends – an expensive and unnecessary luxury for the Dover-Calais service which is so different in character to the requirements and demands of the British Columbian routes.

The 2006 Ro-Ro Conference also saw a presentation concerning hull efficiency given by the Turku-based company, DeltaMarin. This proved to be of tremendous benefit during the planning and building of P&O's new ferries and an excellent relationship was duly forged between the two companies.

THE DESIGN IS BORN

There followed a series of internal meetings and meetings with naval architects. During the time that P&O Ferries was part of the P&O Group, Burness Corlett's Three Quays Group of maritime consultants were used but the company's acquisition by DP World in 2006 allowed them to widen their brief and look elsewhere for new ideas and innovations. With this in mind, and with no 'in-house' naval architect to work with, it was vital that lead consultants were appointed before the project could commence. Consequently, the respected Danish marine architects and engineers Knud E. Hansen were consulted along with Three Quays, BMT and DeltaMarin. Each company was invited to give a presentation and as a result of this, DeltaMarin was appointed in spring 2007.

Throughout the summer and autumn of 2007, the P&O Ferries technical personnel made a series of visits to Finland and gradually plans and specifications for the new ships were drawn up.

The Geneva-based Trollship S.A. specialises in marine brokerage, particularly in ferries and roll on – roll off vessels, and with their assistance an outline tender specification was prepared.

Once this was completed it was simply a matter of asking shipyards to indicate their interest. This came from a variety of worldwide locations: two from South Korea, two from Italy, Croatia, Finland, Germany and Spain. Surprisingly, perhaps, the tender specification elicited little enthusiasm from Japanese yards which were very busy satisfying the demands of their own domestic market.

Now using the expertise of Oslo-based brokers R.S. Platou (part of the Stewart Group), important advice was forthcoming during meetings with DeltaMarin and a final tender specification document was produced. This included several additional items such as glass lifts between the passenger decks, seven escalators to carry passengers from the vehicle decks into the accommodation and cruise ship style side overhangs at the vessels' after ends. It was realised from the start that there were certain items on the company 'wish list' that would not be part of the final brief as there was a requirement to 'cut their cloth' according to the available budget that had been allocated for the creation of the new Super-Ferries. It was also originally planned to move the ships' superstructure further forward to provide a viewing platform but this was later modified.

However, for all concerned with the design and construction of the twin ships, the project proved to be extremely rewarding as for the first time, they were given a clean sheet of paper and were able to take an entirely new look at the construction of these highly specialised vessels which are built to serve on the most demanding short-sea route of all. The fresh and open-minded approach has

The double-ended BC Ferries vessel *Queen of Surrey* leaving Horseshoe Bay (Vancouver). At one time P&O evaluated the use of this type of vessel on the Dover Strait. *(John Hendy)*

provided a number of ground-breaking advances in ferry design and in some respects they are unique.

Each of the short-listed yards were spoken with at length and input into their design resources became an important part of the negotiating process. The yards included Italy's Fincantieri and Nuovi Cantieri Apuania. DSME (Daewoo Shipbuilding and Marine Engineering) of Okpo in South Korea, Aker Finnyards of Rauma in Finland and the Croatian yard, Brodosplit. At the completion of this important stage, it was difficult to separate Aker and DSME but Aker's undertaking of an earlier delivery and the quality premium paid to build in Europe proved to be the deciding factors. A letter of

A number of carefully chosen ferries were used as reference ships before work on the interior planning commenced. The comfortable and classic surroundings of the Club Lounges of the *Pride of Kent* and *Pride of Canterbury* set the designers a standard on which they could build. *(John Hendy)*

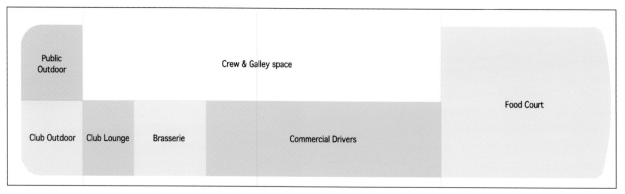

Logistical Layout: Deck 9.

intent was signed in June 2008 and the contract to build yard numbers 1367 and 1368 was signed on 7th August 2008.

CUSTOM BUILT

When building new ships, due to simple matters of economics, many ferry operators turn to a yard and opt for a standard design package with standard fittings sourced from a limited number of contractors. What was unusual in this present build process was that P&O Ferries were able to present their own advanced plans to Aker for a unique pair of ships. It has been seen on many occasions that if ferries are to be successful on any route, they must be custom built to serve it. The Dover-Calais operation is so specialist and intensive with short crossing times and quick turn-rounds in port that any standard shipyard design simply would not do. If there is any route around the British Isles that demands specialist ships then it is undoubtedly this one.

To take one simple example: the ships' storing arrangements. The usual practice has been to load the stores onto pallets which are then driven onto the ferry's main vehicle deck where they are unloaded into the stores below – a time-consuming business which can delay the ship's turn-round time in port and cause a knock-on effect to other vessels waiting to use that particular berth. The new ships have a hatch on the main vehicle decks under which is a huge lift into which a whole lorry will drop so that the unloading can take place on passage to Calais. This saves essential time in port and

allows the ships' schedules to be adhered to without any unnecessary delays.

On 3rd November it was announced that the Aker Yards would become STX Europe to reflect the entry of the South Korean-based STX Business Group as principal shareholder in the company during summer 2008. The company is listed on the Oslo stock exchange.

At Dover, the final Phase 6 drawings were duly approved at the end of February 2009 ready for the first steel for yard number 1367 to be cut in March. With the keel laid on 25th August, construction using the latest prefabricated methods proceeded at pace. Prefabricated hull sections, each about 325 tons in weight, were fitted with key components such as cabling and pipework and moved by tractor from their construction halls before being lifted into the dry dock where the ship was assembled. The yard used a 400-ton crane enabling larger construction modules to be assembled locally while other modules were floated in on heavy lift ships from Turku and Gdansk.

Within an amazing ten months of the keel being laid, the ship was floated out of her dry dock on 8th June 2010 and following trials and fitting out, finally left Rauma on 5th January 2011. Meanwhile, the second ship should be nine months behind.

INTERIORS

Plans for the ships' interiors were provided by the lead consultants SMC Design who have gained much experience in

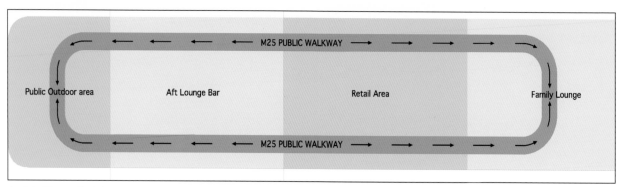

Logistical Layout Deck 8.

High quality computer generated images were available at an early stage to show the public the size and shape of things to come. *(P&O Ferries)*

providing the public rooms for a number of well-known cruise ships including Cunard's *Queen Mary 2* and in the refits of the *Queen Elizabeth 2* as well as various P&O Cruises, Norwegian Cruise Line and Princess Cruises vessels. Their involvement in the ferry industry has recently concerned the public rooms in Viking Line's *Viking XPRS* and signage in the Color Line vessel *Color Fantasy*. In 2001, SMC Design had been involved with the fitting out of both the public rooms and signage of P&O North Sea Ferries *Pride of Hull* and *Pride of Rotterdam*. With this pedigree, it is hardly surprising that SMC's designs for the new Dover ships have more than a hint of the cruise ship concept about them.

Whereas, recent French new-builds for the Dover-Calais crossing display an asymmetrical floor plan with all passenger access between the forward and after parts of the ship only via the starboard side, the new P&O ships boast what was referred to during the early stages of design as, the 'M25 concept'. Just as with the London gyratory, passenger flows will move in either direction around the complete range of on-board services and retail outlets but on a marble composite floor, similar to that used in Heathrow's Terminal 5. Unlike the M25, however, traffic jams are not anticipated!

The galleys (kitchens) have been supplied by Loipart who have

The Finnish ferry *Viking XPRS* is an STX build and was also used as a reference ship by SMC Design. *(STX Europe)*

The ferries of the future

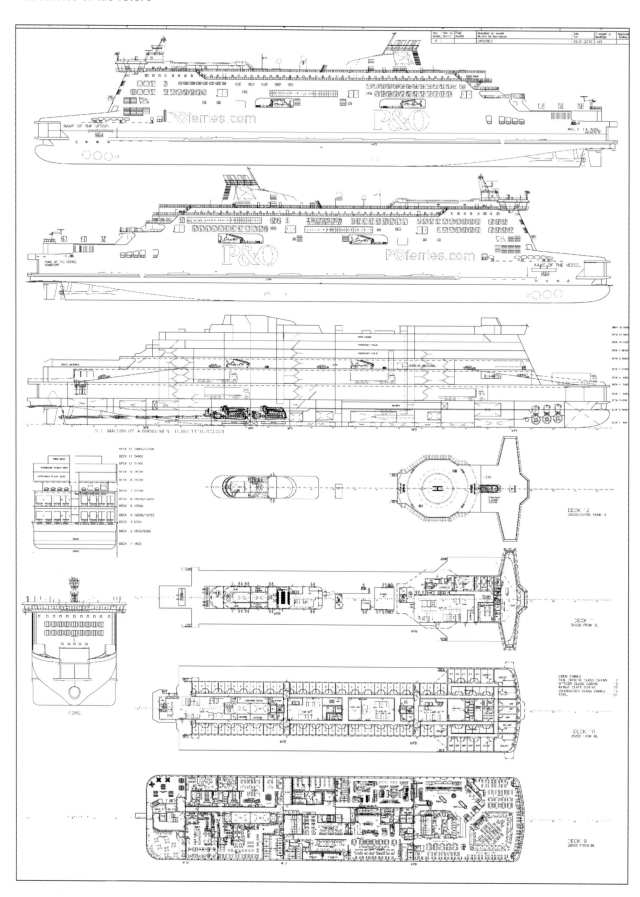

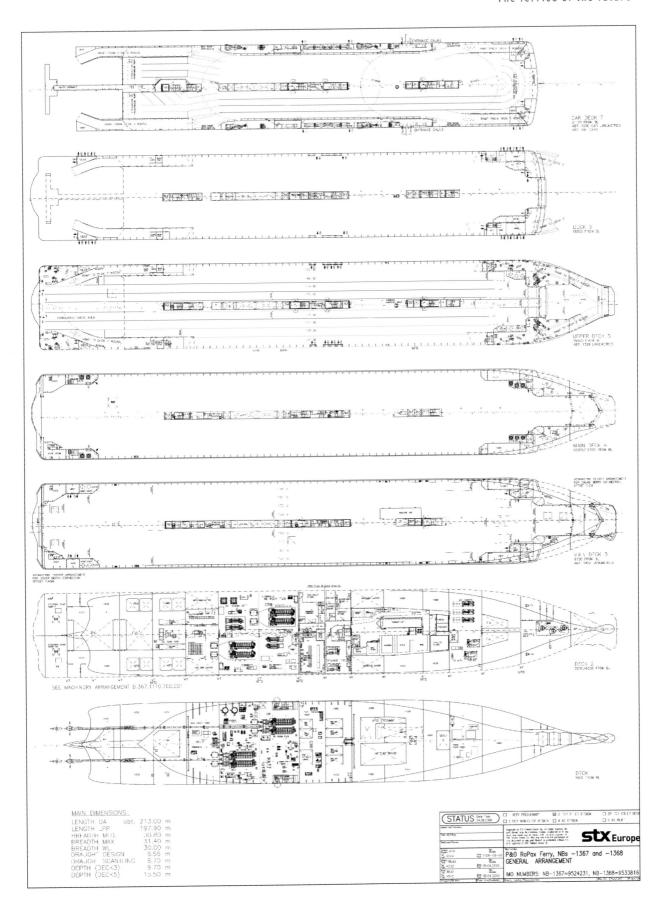

MAIN DIMENSIONS:

LENGTH OA   abt. 213.00 m
LENGTH PP   197.90 m
BREADTH MLD.   30.80 m
BREADTH MAX.   31.40 m
BREADTH WL.   30.00 m
DRAUGHT DESIGN   6.55 m
DRAUGHT SCANTLING   6.70 m
DEPTH (DECK3)   9.70 m
DEPTH (DECK5)   15.50 m

STATUS

stx Europe

P&O RoPax Ferry, NBs -1367 and -1368
GENERAL ARRANGEMENT

IMO NUMBERS: NB-1367=9524231, NB-1368=9533816

Leaving the Kentish coast astern, the *Spirit of Britain* makes her way across the Dover Strait to Calais. *(FotoFlite)*

Spirit of Britain

The ferries of the future

The Estonian cruise ferry *Galaxy* is another STX product and was also used as a reference ship in terms of the quality of materials. The ship is seen approaching Stockholm in June 2010. *(John Hendy)*

supplied similar installations to a number of Finnish-built cruise ships.

SMC have successfully completed many retail space's. However KKD were appointed after P&O research trips to Heathrow T5. The Finnish company Merima were sub-contracted to build the ships' interiors having previously worked for Celebrity Cruises and Norwegian Cruise Line as well as on the Tallink ferry *Baltic Princess* which was built at the Aker yard in Helsinki and the *Color Super Speed 1* and *Color Super Speed II* at Rauma in 2008. STX Europe will provide all the crew cabins as they are made in modules and can be placed into position with the minimum of difficulty.

In the design of the ships' interiors, the Tallink cruise ferry *Galaxy* was used as a reference ship in the food court, grill house and family lounge areas while the *Pride of Kent* also served as a point of reference for other interior design work, notably the Club Lounge and Brasserie. Much of the artwork is from DP World's headquarters in Palace Street, London and the ships both feature a P&O colour palette with a display of P&O memorabilia not only emphasising their Britishness but also the strong sense of maritime history associated with the P&O brand name. This is to be applauded.

TECHNICAL

On the technical front, the German company MAN Nutzfahrzeuge AG of Nuremburg was appointed to supply the ships' powerful

marine diesel engines while the contract for the twin rudders was awarded to Becker Marine Systems of Hamburg. The ships' fin stabilisers are provided by Blohm + Voss of Hamburg. With previous experience of using Wartsila engines in their Dover-based ships, the company used the expertise of their Hull-based engineers to advise them with the new MAN engines. The North Sea engineers advised the technical team on the Wartsila 46C engines which are installed in the *Pride of Hull* and *Pride of Rotterdam*. (see page 92)

No fewer than five propulsion types were evaluated before the tried and tested arrangement of four main engines, two propellers and three bow thrusts was chosen. This was regarded as a proven system on the high volume short-sea crossings as a propulsion system needs to be reliable and resilient, operating as it does for about 350 days x 10 trips a year on the Dover-Calais route. Additionally, the adopted system has electronic rather than mechanical ignition with better combustion, spares are readily available with plenty of manufacturers' support and training was also available from the manufacturers for the crews of both ships. The operational profile includes intensive manoeuvring, some of which is inefficient with conventional diesel engines. The main engines use common rail technology which means better fuel combustion which in turn reduces the amount of unburnt fuel that discharges into the atmosphere and settles as hydro carbons in the harbour.

An energy-saving study was carried out during the early stages of the basic ferry design. This identified many possibilities on the system and equipment side. One clear result was that the control of all systems should be as good as possible e.g. with the variable speed pumps. An important issue on the Dover-Calais route is that waste heat from the exhaust gas boilers is available for about 60-65% of each day. It was therefore decided to design the heavy fuel oil storage system so that the sea temperature in the tanks is kept higher than normal and that during port times the temperature does not fall too low. Thus, there is no requirement to use the oil-fired boilers during the brief periods of turn-round in the ports. Furthermore, the waste heat from the cooling water system also enables fresh water to be generated for technical uses on board which negates the requirement to bunker and use fresh water natural resources.

Following extensive Dutch tank tests to determine the ideal hull form for the new ferries, a totally new design for a water depth of 30 metres was formulated. The ships, therefore, are built to suit the depth of water in the English Channel and are designed for shallow water use. The engines for the first ship were delivered in November 2009 and the vessel was built around them. One of the inevitable risks that owners and operators face is that a proportion of passengers and crew may find a ship uncomfortable. This can lead to a poor reputation, loss of trade, loss of resale value and, in extreme cases, an adverse impact on health and safety. The use of noise and vibration prediction and measurement tools during design and construction can minimise this risk and at the conclusion of building, and before and during operation, it is important to have an independent industry standard to meet.

Lloyd's Register provides a Marine Design Appraisal assisting in the streamlining of a design during the construction process in order to increase confidence in the ship's future performance. They work with clients to help improve the quality, safety, environmental and business performance and P&O's new twins are built to DNV Cruise Comfort level 2.

The vessels have been designed to be as environmentally friendly as possible and qualify for the Lloyd's Register 'Green Passport'. Although their fuel consumption will be similar to that of the vessels which they are replacing, their payload is approximately double and their hydrodynamically efficient hull form coupled with their MAN 7L48/60 medium speed main engines ensures that they both reduce fuel consumption and give fewer CO_2 emissions. The three bow thrust units (thereby minimising expensive use of tugs during the berthing procedure) will also give high levels of manoeuvrability in port.

SAFE RETURN TO PORT

During the preliminary work involved in the construction of the new ships, the International Maritime Organisation's Maritime Safety Committee issued a notice on new 'Safe Return to Port' (SRtP) regulations (MSC 1/ Circ 1214 – 15th December 2006). These were necessary due to the huge growth in size of cruise ships, many of which have become floating resorts but until now, the ferry industry had not been involved in this development. However, since July 2010, these new regulations are required for all passenger

Irish Ferries' Aker/STX-built *Ulysees* was a further reference ship and incorporates a similar upper car deck loading arrangement. She is seen arriving at Dublin. *(Miles Cowsill)*

The ferries of the future

The fulfilment of many years' planning and dedication from P&O Ferries; on 9th January 2011, the *Spirit of Britain* finally passes through the eastern entrance of Dover Harbour. The dream had become a reality. *(Brian Powell)*

ships with a length of over 120 metres and carrying 36 or more passengers. The ship must be able to return to port in the event that any of her compartments are destroyed by water or fire. The new ships are the first ferries in the world to comply with the International Maritime Organisation's 'Safe Return to Port' requirements, ahead of the international compliance date.

Ferries are mainly built for short international voyages of a maximum of 200 miles from a place of safety or for long international voyages with a maximum of 600 miles from a place of safety. Whereas cruise ships are involved in unlimited trading, the new requirements helped to clarify the scope of the necessary endurance required of today's modern ferry fleets. Initial work was done to determine the principles to be employed in SRtP based upon the operating area of the vessel, the time required to reach a safe haven and the survivability and fire requirements. The main work was defining all spaces including the equipment in them and cabling passing through them. To simplify matters somewhat, whereas most four-engined traditional ships would in all likelihood be fitted with all engines in one compartment, in P&O's new-builds the portside engines are sited in an adjacent compartment to those on the starboard side. Should the vessel ever be holed or disabled by fire in an engine compartment, then the surviving engines should be able to propel her back to port without the need of towage.

EVACUATION

Evacuation is also an important factor in modern ship design. Whereas older ships were fitted with traditional lifeboats, these have gradually been replaced by Marine Escape Systems (MES). In the *Spirit of Britain* and *Spirit of France*, the evacuation arrangements consist of six Marine Escape Systems which provide an equivalent level of safety to a conventional solution under SOLAS regulation class III which applies to vessels which will at no time be operating more than 20 nautical miles from land. The six MES stations have a total raft capacity of 2,750 persons and 10% additional capacity in davit-handled rafts for infants and disabled passengers. In addition there are four rescue craft for towing the life rafts which are manufactured by RFD Marinark.

CARGO SPACES

P&O's key business objective is to deliver 'economies of scale' rather than 'like for like' of the vessels which the two new ships are replacing. With an overall length of 213 metres against the 169 metres of the earlier generation ships, it can be seen that their payload is considerably larger.

Three dedicated vehicle decks are provided. Decks 3 and 5 accommodate approximately 170 trucks in 2,750 lane metres without any encumbrance of mezzanine decks. The twin decks are

The ferries of the future

Deck 7 is the dedicated motorists' vehicle deck. Of lower headroom than the twin lorry decks below, this is the view looking forward. Notice the blue, yellow and red stripes on the central casing that each correspond to the stairways of those colours. *(SMC)*

double height to allow the passage of freight and therefore, there are no Decks 4 or 6. Both freight decks accommodate eight lanes of traffic (four either side of the central casing) with an unprecedented 3.2-metre lane width in the six outside lanes. The lanes closest to the central casing have a 3-metre width that, until now, has been the norm with other ferries in the English Channel. However, on Deck 5 the inside lanes give 179 metres lane length, whereas these decrease towards the ships' sides to 174 metres, 146 metres and 109 metres. This is due to the positioning of the ramps to Deck 7, the ventilators and winches. Dangerous or hazardous cargoes are stored at the after end of Deck 5 which has open access and is not enclosed. On Deck 3, the inside lanes are both 189-metres long, followed by lanes of 175 metres, 161 metres and 137 metres against the ships' sides. The extra lane width provided will make parking easier and considerably enhance the loading and unloading processes. The port inside lane of Deck 3 houses the trailer lift which drops to Deck 2 where trailers' contents are removed to the adjacent stores and refrigerators.

Above the twin freight decks, Deck 7 holds approximately 195 cars in 1,000 lane metres. Once again, four lanes of traffic are accommodated either side of the central casing, each with a width of 2.4 metres. Motorcycles have their own allocated spaces at the far ends of this deck. It can be seen that Deck 7 is narrower than the twin freight decks below as not only the Calais entrance doors for

foot passengers but also fan rooms and each ship's four rescue craft are recessed outside the car spaces.

Access to the passenger accommodation is via five stairways and three lifts in the centre casing and four stairs from Deck 7 upwards. In such large ships, it is suspected that some passengers may experience problems with locating their vehicles at the end of each Channel crossing. A system of colour coding the principal stairs from Deck 7 in P&O colours – poppy red, sunflower yellow or lavender blue – has therefore been adopted which should go some way to alleviating this problem. At the after end, the Dover 'skywalk' allows access to the ship for foot passengers who will climb the 'blue' stairs into the accommodation.

Deck 7 is linked to Deck 5 by two fixed ramps port and starboard, fore and aft. With the eventual construction of the new ferry ports at both Dover and Calais, provision will be made to allow cars to drive on and off at the side and space has been allocated in the ships' shell plating at the top of the ramps to allow for side doors (two on the port side and two on the starboard) to be inserted. This will be very much a 'first' for both ports and will certainly permit the speedier handling of cars while completely separating freight from tourist traffic.

PORT INFRASTRUCTURE

Throughout the history of the operation of vehicle ferries across

Clear and unambiguous airport-style signage is a feature of the new ships. *(SMC)*

53

The ferries of the future

The *Spirit of Britain* is seen departing from Calais on the inward leg of her maiden voyage on 21st January 2011. *(John Hendy)*

the Dover Strait, the port operators have, out of necessity, always worked closely with the ferry designers. As ferries have become larger and capacity has increased, new and wider linkspans have been provided in both Dover and Calais in order to allow the greater beam of the latest ferries an acceptable port fit.

P&O Ferries' new ships each have the largest beam of any ferry in the English Channel and at 31.4 metres are therefore potentially too large to fit any of the present linkspans. In 1987 when the *Pride of Dover* and *Pride of Calais* entered service, they also were faced with a similar problem and berthed at an angle until new linkspans were provided. Initially, the 'Spirit' class of 1980 also had to contend without suitable berth fit which also necessitated them berthing at a slight angle in order to dock successfully.

At the time of writing, both Dover Harbour Board and the Calais Chamber of Commerce are committed to building completely new ferry facilities which will enable ships of the size of the new P&O vessels to berth with ease. In the short term, the problem will be overcome by providing an offset bow 'spade' (offset by 1.2 metres for berthing at Calais) and an offset stern 'spade' (by 1.45 metres) to allow port fit at Dover's Eastern Docks. Once the new ferry terminals are opened, the 'spades' (both fore and aft) will be repositioned to fit the latest linkspans. Until the construction of larger berths, the ships' beams of 31.4 metres should not cause any major operation problems apart from having to berth 'port-side to' at Dover and 'starboard side to' at Calais. Eventually berths 9, 8 and

7 will be modified at Calais while Dover's berths 9, 7 and 3 will be fitted with side fendering to allow a better port fit.

At this stage in time, it would have been impossible for P&O to have further increased the size of their new ships as they represent the maximum size that the port facilities in both Dover and Calais can presently accommodate. The ships are therefore designated, 'Dover Max'.

As it has been seen, the introduction of these new ferries has posed a number of problems for shipbuilders, ship owners and port operators alike. Efficient operation on the Dover-Calais link demands short turn-round times in port and yet with almost double the capacity of the ships they replace, how can the extra traffic be handled without increasing the overall port time?

Technical innovations within the new ships are wider cargo doors, fixed ramps to fixed decks, the absence of mezzanine decks which effectively serve to slow down the loading of any ferry, electric winches and the ability to speed up the lowering of the shore side linkspans. In addition, P&O commissioned a Port Turn Round Project to review current procedures, identify improvements and provide an estimate of time required to turn the new vessels around in both Dover and Calais. Both these initiatives have assisted to identify areas of 'best practice' both on board and on shore so that a fully integrated operations team can deliver best customer service. As a result of this work, improvements were immediately implemented in the existing fleet thereby giving an early benefit for this project. It has been found that port time can be reduced by 5 minutes which allows for a reduction in speed of about 1 knot and thereby gives a substantial fuel saving per sailing.

SUMMARY

It can be seen that the production of these ships has involved a vast amount of industry input from a wide and diverse collection of experts during their preparation, construction and finishing stages. In the preparation period, P&O also sought the views of its customers and their ideas and suggestions were all evaluated before the plans were finalised.

The result of these endeavours is a pair of ships which represent a complete and total re-evaluation of the requirements of the premier link between Dover and Calais. Whereas previously, ship designs have largely tended to be 'in house' and innovation (if any) was invariably added to existing designs on a somewhat larger scale, much of what we see in these new ships is totally new.

They are the largest and most impressive ferries ever built for service across the English Channel. Their hull design has been optimised for the Dover-Calais route to ensure maximum performance and good manoeuvring characteristics. Special attention has been paid to environmentally friendly and energy-efficient solutions and safety, and the ships are the first car/passenger ferries to meet the IMO's Safe Return to Port requirements. They also meet the requirements of the Lloyd's

Register Green Passport scheme.

The *Spirit of Britain* and *Spirit of France* are truly, the 'Ferries of the Future'!

Spirit of Britain - Passenger Decks 8 and 9

The ship's main passenger areas are to be found on Decks 8 and 9, with Deck 8 being entirely devoted to passenger use.

DECK 8

At the forward end of the ship is **The Family Lounge** with its central performance area in which children's entertainers will perform during busy periods. Overhead television screens playing cartoons are aimed to keep the children happy while special play areas are designed to cater for the very young. Toilets are thoughtfully provided nearby and P&O's commitment to the environment is much in evidence, as it is throughout the ship, with the provision of special recycling bins. A Family Lounge bar/coffee shop provides hot and cold drinks and sandwiches as well as alcoholic beverages.

A total of 341 passenger seats are provided in The Family Lounge and a special feature is the provision of panoramic windows which allow the area to flood with light while providing excellent views of the passing seascape. The use of warm reds and oranges throughout, together with subtle lighting, assists in the creation of a bright and happy family atmosphere.

Taken from the bridge of the *Pride of Canterbury* during berthing trials on 14th January 2011, this view illustrates the size of the new *Spirit of Britain* compared with the *Pride of Calais* which has served the company faithfully since 1987. *(Captain Steve Johnson)*.

Family Lounge *(SMC)*

The ferries of the future

Moving aft, the central area of the ship is occupied by the **Retail Area** with Arcades either side allowing access to the after areas of the ship. The new 'Shop & Collect' tax-free store stocks all the popular brands together with luxury premium items, perfumes, toys, sweets, books, magazines and important travel essentials such as conversion plugs, maps and breakdown kits. With coffee stations, ATMs and vending machines nearby, the new ship offers everything expected of a large shopping centre. Either side, the **Arcades** each have seating for 172 passengers. On the starboard side of the ship, the **Bureau de Change** and **Information Desk** are to be found while the port side area leading into the Aft Lounge boasts a **Video Games** area.

The port and starboard arcades lead to the **Aft Lounge** which has a light, open and more contemporary feel with a more restrained, cooler, blue palette used to upholster much of the furniture. The Aft Lounge can be split into two in order that one area can be closed off during periods when passenger numbers do not warrant the full strength of facilities being made available. Thus Aft Lounge 1 is sited on the port side and accommodates 188 passengers while Aft Lounge 2 is on the starboard side and holds a similar number of passengers. At the back of the Aft Lounge, a central coffee bar is sited so that half is situated in area 1 while the other half is in Aft Lounge 2; each has a small lounge for 33 passengers which again can be isolated in times of low passenger uptake. When not in use, the dividing screens are cleverly stored away out of sight but, if required, can be rolled back into position in minutes. The starboard side coffee bar in Aft Lounge 2 contains a splendid builders' model of the ship with flags presented by STX Europe and the Mayor of Rauma where she was built. The coffee shop provides alcoholic drinks in addition to coffee, tea and sandwich-type snacks. Throughout the ship are a series of artwork panels that tell the story of her construction in addition to artwork based on iconic British landmarks (the Angel of the North, Stonehenge, Big Ben, the London 'gherkin' etc). Elsewhere, other panels tell the story of

The contemporary lighting fixtures on board the new ships are worthy of note. *(John Hendy)*

P&O's 170-year heritage while a collection of holiday memorabilia is also on view.

Doors from the Aft Lounge lead onto the **Outside Deck** which provides views across the ship's stern. Special non-slip decking has been provided with wooden railings and deck furniture while telescopes have even been supplied to assist passengers with their ship spotting! During the summer, a special seasonal **Outside Bar** will be open to provide passengers with drinks. This is very much a 'first' for P&O and allows passengers the benefit of remaining outside without the need to return to the ship's interior to buy drinks, snacks and ice creams – all very much in keeping with the cruise experience which P&O Ferries seek to provide.

DECK 9

Approximately half of Deck 9 is devoted to passenger space. At the forward end is **The Food Court** which can seat a total of 451 passengers – 287 in the lower level and a further 150 in the upper level. This arrangement has been made in order to provide a view of the sea for all diners, even those sitting in the centre of this area.

The new ships have something for everyone. Here is the entrance to Vegas Slots on Deck 8. *(SMC)*

A detail in the Family Lounge showing bright fabrics and comfortable seating. *(John Hendy)*

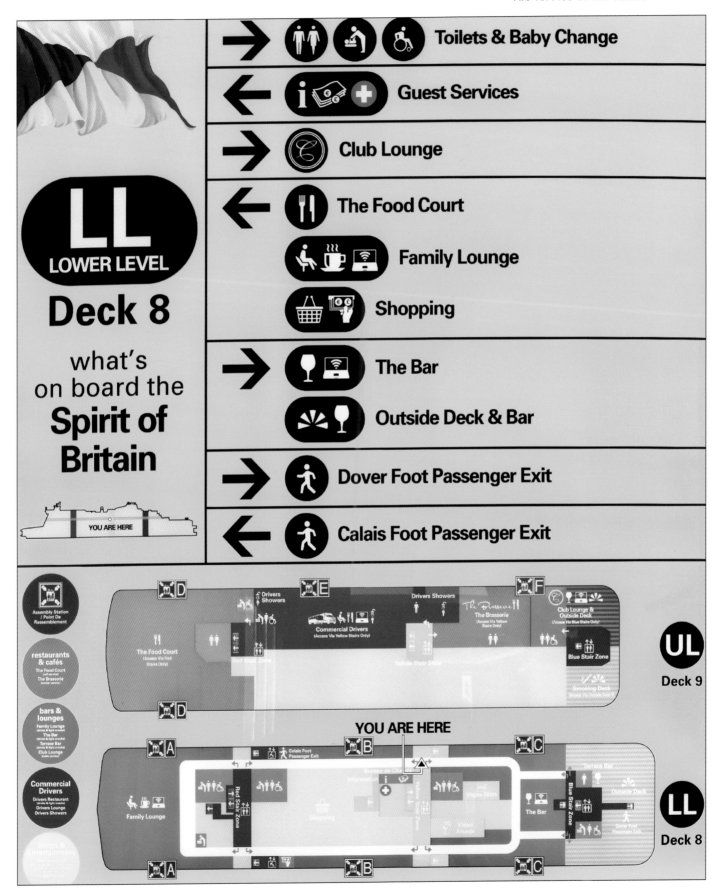

LL
LOWER LEVEL

Deck 8

what's on board the **Spirit of Britain**

YOU ARE HERE

→ Toilets & Baby Change

← Guest Services

→ Club Lounge

← The Food Court

Family Lounge

Shopping

→ The Bar

Outside Deck & Bar

→ Dover Foot Passenger Exit

← Calais Foot Passenger Exit

Assembly Station / Point De Rassemblement

restaurants & cafés
The Food Court (self service)
The Brasserie (waiter service)

bars & lounges
Family Lounge (drinks & light snacks)
The Bar
Terrace Bar (drinks & light snacks)
Club Lounge (public service)

Commercial Drivers
Drivers Restaurant (drinks & light snacks)
Drivers Lounge
Drivers Showers

Shops & Entertainment

Drivers Showers

Drivers Showers

Commercial Drivers (Access Via Yellow Stairs Only)

The Food Court (Access Via Red Stairs Only)

Red Stair Zone

Yellow Stair Zone

The Brasserie (Access Via Yellow Stairs Only)

Club Lounge & Outside Deck (Access Via Blue Stairs Only)

Blue Stair Zone

Smoking Deck (Access Via Outside Deck)

UL Deck 9

YOU ARE HERE

Calais Foot Passenger Exit

Dover de Chan

Information

Family Lounge

Red Stair Zone

Shopping

Yellow Stair Zone

Vegas Slots

Video Arcade

Terrace Bar

Outside Deck

The Bar

Blue Stair Zone

Dover Foot Passenger Exit

LL Deck 8

The Bureau de change and Information desks are adjacent to each other on Deck 8. [SMC]

Information

Bureau de change

The Aft Lounge (port side) which is visually more restrained than the forward Family Lounge. *(SMC)*

This view from the port side of the Aft Lounge's cafe/bar shows the running tracks (to the left of the exit sign) along which partitions can be slid in order to close off this area during quiet periods. *(SMC)*

Another view of the Aft Lounge on Deck 8 showing an assortment of images all of which capture the 'Spirit of Britain'. *(SMC)*

Illuminating the *Spirit of Britain*. These delicate lamps assist in the creation of a cruise ferry ambience. *(John Hendy)*

From a practical viewpoint, the upper level can again be closed off during periods when fewer passengers are travelling.

Hot food is available throughout the day including P&O's famous all-day English breakfast and fish & chips. For those simply seeking a snack, a 'Grab and Go' facility has also been provided offering sandwiches, paninis, muffins, pastries and salads.

Moving towards the stern of the ship, most of the port side is given over to the crew. As with all P&O vessels using Dover, the ship operates with two complete live-aboard crews, one of which is at work while the other rests. As the ship is their home, it is vital to provide them with their own lounge, shop, recreation room and eating area (mess). Right at the after end of Deck 9 on the port side is an area of **Outside Deck** on which passengers can smoke – the only area on the vessel where they are permitted to do so.

The starboard side of the ship meanwhile is dedicated to **Routemasters**, a specially designed area provided for the benefit of lorry drivers who value the Channel break as a relaxation period between long stretches behind the wheel. It is of interest that whereas the majority of tourist vehicles head southwards from Calais, the majority of lorry drivers travel eastwards. Routemasters allows drivers to shower and provides them with rest areas, their own shop, a cafeteria and their own dedicated outside deck space with smoking and non-smoking sections.

Further aft on the starboard side is the **Brasserie**, a waiter-service bistro providing British cuisine and fine wines for up to 70

The forward area of the Food Court with views across the ship's bow. *(SMC)*

The Food Court offers a variety of meals which include traditional P&O favourites and 'grab and go'. [SMC]

The ferries of the future

The Routemasters (lorry drivers) lounge is on Deck 9 and contains this bank of reclining sun loungers looking out towards the sea. Notice the glass screen behind with its tyre tread pattern. *(SMC)*

passengers in a quiet and restful area. The menu is designed to suit all appetites and tastes and is open throughout the day for breakfast, lunch and dinner. Many reproduction posters illustrating the heyday of P&O cruising line the walls and are a reminder of the company's illustrious past.

From the Brasserie we pass into the **Club Lounge**. This is in effect a First Class area in which, for a small supplement, up to 50 passengers can relax in a luxurious and peaceful setting in deep and comfortable armchairs and settees upholstered in browns and

blues. With its brown laminated panelled walls, upmarket light fittings and floor to ceiling curtains, it exudes the air of a traditional gentlemen's club in the best P&O between-the-wars tradition. The area is supplied with its own bar and champagne, tea, coffee and light refreshments are constantly available.

For the first time, the Club Lounge is given its own dedicated **Club Lounge Viewing Deck** which is bound to prove a great bonus during the summer season and warmer periods of weather.

The cafeteria space in the Routemasters area on Deck 9. *(Miles Cowsill)*

Lorry drivers have their own dedicated area of the ships including a shower block and wet room. *(SMC)*

The blue stairs are at the ship's after end. *(SMC)*

P&O
Ferries

The Brasserie on Deck 9 is a contemporary space with heritage P&O posters on the bulkheads. *(SMC)*

The Club Lounge is tastefully fitted with subdued lighting, wood-effect panelling, comfortable furniture and architectural mouldings all aiming to recapture the glory days of P&O's history. *(SMC)*

chapter
five

SMC Design

Alan Stewart - Senior Designer/Project Manager

Andrew Collier - Managing Director

Thoroughly researched to withstand the test of time

SMC Design was invited by P&O Ferries to submit initial concept design ideas and principles for two new short-sea vessels and following a review process, we were fortunate enough to be appointed lead interior architects in May 2007. By being involved early on, SMC Design had the opportunity to be involved in the initial development work with the entire new-build team. This enabled us to work in an extremely fluid way to produce block plan layouts and designs based on P&O Ferries' core business requirements.

After the P&O Ferries board approval of the public space configurations, we worked in unison with naval architects DeltaMarin to produce a more detailed set of general arrangement drawings. This put P&O Ferries in the strong position of going out to tender with shipyards worldwide with a clearly defined set of plans and specifications that set out their exact requirements.

Another benefit of such an early appointment was that SMC Design was included in P&O Ferries' research development programme. This involved in-depth studies being carried out on the existing fleet's operational processes, with all aspects of the business being subject to examination, ranging from the on-board hotel offer to cleaning and maintenance issues. As part of these studies, the on-board crew numbers were reviewed to see if the vessels could operate more efficiently and in response to the quantity of passengers on board at any given time. This was to lead to the adoption of a plan that integrated flexible spaces which would meet these changing demands.

A further part of this research programme involved sailing on other European ferry routes to see what, if any, other design strategies were in place that would benefit the new ships' business propositions. Various innovative ideas including passenger flow through to opportunistic revenue solutions were studied and reviewed to see if and how they could be implemented into a 90-minute crossing operation.

The main challenge with this type of vessel is the limited turnaround time both when in dock and in transit. With this in mind our main focus was to find the most effective and quickest way for passengers to navigate their way around the ships. The overall aim was to create a clear and logical layout which ensured the best possible passenger flow. Alongside this we had to consider the varied demographic of passengers found on these short-sea crossings. Profiles range from young family groups to coach parties as well as the single traveller. We therefore had to combine this easy-to-navigate layout with spaces and environments that would meet all passenger needs.

This ease of navigation begins on the car deck, an area that needs to be cleared as quickly as possible. This is achieved via three main sets of stairs and lifts each individually colour coded and including memorable imagery to assist with passenger

The light and airy Family Lounge is fitted with large panoramic windows and brightly coloured contemporary furniture. *(SMC)*

recognition when returning to their vehicles. An essential part of creating the most effective passenger flow and orientation is signage. Large-scale airport-style yellow and black pictogram signs are used from the car decks up into the public decks. This type of signage was adopted as it is easily understood by most European nationalities and is a style that most people are familiar with. It was quickly established that the upper Deck 9 was best suited to contain all the 'destination' areas such as the Club Lounge, Brasserie, Routemasters Lounge, and Food Court. Passengers usually have reasons to visit these spaces and so they do not require walk-through access. By having this direct access it allows these spaces to become quieter locations where people want to spend more time. The facilities on offer to the commercial drivers have greatly increased. This space now contains its own food court, TV lounge with multilingual channels, relaxation lounge with daybeds and an outdoor observation balcony. The drivers can also have a shower during the crossing in one of 24 specially designed self-contained shower pods.

A large international self-service Food Court with a free flow servery and a Brasserie-style waiter service restaurant cover passenger dining options. A separate Premium Club Lounge with a

private outdoor area was created for passengers willing to pay extra for a quieter and more exclusive crossing experience.

Deck 8 is where the main walk-through rooms are located. To ensure these spaces could be easily and quickly accessed, we developed a circular walkway that became known as the 'M25' and is clearly defined by a composite stone floor finish. This circular layout ensures that passengers are able to orientate around this deck with ease. To further assist with orientation, the sightlines have also been purposely kept as open as possible to create interiors that allow the passengers to intuitively locate themselves and at the same time view the variety of facilities offered on board.

This deck contains the forward facing Family Lounge and allows the family groups to 'nest' whilst the Aft Bar Lounge is aimed at the older passenger and includes both a slot machine zone and video arcade. The Retail area was positioned mid-ships as it is the most visited space on board; being located centrally it encourages and maximises access to the retail products on offer.

One major benefit of this type of layout is that it creates large clear central spaces and to enhance these open spaces we also worked closely with the shipyard to maximise the amount of glazing along Decks 8 and 9. These large panoramic windows not

Computer generated graphics showing key passenger areas

Right: The outside deck space at the after end of Deck 8 stretches across the full width of the ships.

Top left: The red stairs linking Decks 8 and 9.

Left: The Brasserie on Deck 9.

Above: The Costa Coffee outlet in the Family Lounge on Deck 8.

Top: The Deck 8 coffee shop and bar and the Aft Lounge can be divided into two in order that one area can be closed off during quiet periods.

Left: The comfortable Club Lounge at the after end of Deck 9.

Top: The Aft Lounge and Video Arcade on the left.

Centre left: The Food Court with its simple and practical layout.

Left: Recliners in the Routemasters area.

Above: Ladies toilet area.

Top: The Food Court showing the centrally raised area providing everyone with a view of the sea.

Left: The Retail Area occupies the centre of Deck 8.

SMC Design

The Club Lounge offers its clientele their own exclusive area of outside deck space on Deck 9. *(SMC)*

only became a real feature for the ships but also enabled us to install an energy efficient lighting system. This works by using photosensitive light-harvesting cells which continually analyse the amount of natural daylight coming in through the windows and adjusts the light settings automatically to control the amount of artificial light required. This should make considerable energy savings over the ships' lifespans.

The P&O Ferries brand has also had a major influence in the colour scheme of these new ships with the underlying premise being to raise the brand identity by using the corporate colour palette based on the P&O Ferries flag.

In creating a contemporary essentially British experience for the passenger we have, where possible, used UK-sourced materials and products throughout the ships. This has the added benefit of making future maintenance and replacement easier. Due to the 24/7 nature of the ships, materials were also selected for their durability and ease of maintenance.

Working with P&O Ferries' new-build and on-board services teams at an early stage and in such depth has, we believe, resulted in a pair of thoroughly researched vessels that will meet all their challenges and withstand the test of time.

A corner of the retail area. *(Miles Cowsill)*

The yellow stairs linking the passenger accommodation with the vehicle decks. *(SMC)*

SMC Design is a multi-disciplined design company successfully combining Interior Design, Graphic Design and Artwork Consultancy through many prestigious leisure, retail and hospitality projects. We have a proven track record of designing new build and refurbishment projects of the highest quality from initial concept through to final completion.

Our extensive experience covers innovative designs for atriums, receptions, casinos, lounges, restaurants, bars, retail outlets, kids areas and spas. No project is too big or small. Our belief is that the most important aspect in any design is to understand our clients philosophy, and by doing so allow their dreams to be turned into reality, delivering designs that exceed their expectations.

We would welcome the opportunity to listen to your own future plans and tell you a little about how our passion for design can deliver outstanding solutions for your next new build or refurbishment project, adding real value to your business and building loyalty amongst your customers.

Interior Design, Graphic Design, Artwork Consultancy.

SMC Design Limited
7-10 Charlotte Mews London W1T 4EE UK
Tel: +44 (0)20 7436 6466

www.smc-design.com

chapter SIX

Designed by you ... Built for you

by Simon Johnson
Passenger Services Director

Long before the first steel plates were cut, much detailed, preliminary, research had gone into the new-builds. After highlighting and interviewing the many and diverse groups that will use the ships, from family groups to lorry drivers and from ship's officers to crew involved with the preparation of food, a 'Designed by you – Built for you' concept was formulated as the thousands of thoughts, innovations and ideas were evaluated and laid before the planning team.

'WOW' RATINGS

The top 'Wow' ratings featured an exclusive Club Class deck area, sea views with light and space, more and better freight drivers' showers, clearer signage, a young family section in the family lounge, seat-back TV screens in the freight and coach driver lounge with Satnav journey information displays and the basic need for family-friendly toilet facilities which have been increased by 25% and are provided at the top of every stairwell.

As the ships have been built to provide a break in a journey, it was recognised that they should create a sense of freedom and space after many miles on the road in the confines of a vehicle. In order to assist in this, the four colours of the famous P&O flag were used to offer an immediate 'brand experience' with clean, white vehicle decks and red, yellow and blue stairways leading up into the passenger accommodation. These also form the basis of the ships' interior colour palette and with 2012 being the 175th anniversary of the company's foundation, it provides an excellent and permanent reminder of what is essentially the most British of shipping companies.

BRAND

The brand on board is obviously very important and at every point of the crossing P&O are making sure that their customers know they are travelling with the company. The P&O flag has been given prominence on the outside and inside of the ships as research has shown the house flag has a high recognition to the travelling public. The website has been removed from the exterior to de-clutter it because the internet has matured to the point where customers can easily find P&O on the web. Hence from the very moment that they sight the ships, drive on board, park their cars in a particular zone, climb the stairway into the passenger accommodation, find their way to a seat, seek out the on-board facilities, descend to the vehicle deck, find their car and drive off, the P&O brand will constantly be with them.

The Steering Group to oversee the building of the new ships was led by P&O Ferries' Chief Executive Officer Helen Deeble, ably assisted by John Garner (Fleet & Project Lead), Mike O'Dwyer (On-board Delivery), Simon Johnson (Customer Experience) and Karl Howarth (Financing). Reporting to them were the Delivery Team which were overseen by Programme Manager Mike Langley. The team consisted of colleagues with expertise in freight, yield and planning, finance, marketing, Human Resources, IT, on-board services, ports and fleet. Project Inspection Approval was given by Project Approval Manager, Steve Morant.

Once the internal structure was in place, brokers and builders had to be appointed and the Steering Group nominated the companies which would oversee the ships' design, the P&O branding and the on-board services.

SMC Design were given the brief of 'bright, airy, freedom, space' while DeltaMarin saw to the all-important hull design which reflected the specific needs and requirements of the Dover-Calais passage. Wests Design consultants were awarded the brief of ensuring that throughout the ships, the branding was strong on the P&O colour palette and to create outlet brand guidelines for each of the key areas such as Club, Routemasters, food and beverage outlets and retail outlets.

Following the disappointing asymmetrical designs in the recent ships introduced by P&O's competitors in the Dover Strait, the M25 orbital concept was preferred allowing customers to circumnavigate the entire accommodation on Deck 8 and take in the sea views on both sides of the ship. Kinnersley Kent Design were awarded the job of creating the retail outlet referenced to Bluewater and The Ocean Terminal Shopping Centre in Leith. They were seen as an inspiration in allowing large numbers of people to successfully flow around a central core of shops in a pleasant environment. The company has invested in robust materials throughout and a marble floor has been laid around the ships' own Paris Peripherique.

Externally the company has invested in the outside areas by

installing cruise-style decking, furniture and binoculars with an outside bar providing refreshments on sunny days. Club Class customers, freight drivers and crew have all been given their own dedicated outside spaces in order that everyone can enjoy sea views from inside or outside and watch the iconic White Cliffs of Dover, which was rated as a "wow" by customers as a signal of leaving and arriving into Britain.

Throughout the planning process, good practice and excellence in design was closely monitored in other modern European ferries and no fewer than 15 vessels were visited and industry experts consulted before it was decided to adopt Tallink's *Galaxy* as the core reference ship. Club Class references were taken from the P&O sister ships *Pride of Kent* and *Pride of Canterbury*, windows giving maximum light from *MSC Musica*, Stena's HSS and Norfolkline's Dunkirk vessels, while the display of P&O heritage is from DP World's regional office in London.

SIGNAGE

During a 90-minute crossing, it is essential that passengers unfamiliar with the ships know where to locate the various on-board outlets/facilities and to assist in this, airport-style yellow signage was deemed to be the most appropriate method of 'way finding' with airport-style screens showing eating outlets which is very familiar to customers from anywhere in the world. In order to alleviate queues waiting at the principal retail outlets in the centre of the ships, the Satnav television system will show maps indicating the ships' position with a count down to arrival on passage to alleviate large

The Club Lounge's outside deck area. *(Miles Cowsill)*

Designed by you ... Built for you

numbers of last minute purchasers when passengers realise that their ship is preparing to berth. The provision of the ships' global positioning system should, in theory, allow shoppers to make their purchases throughout the crossings and it is hoped that the avoidance of lengthy queues will increase the on-board spend per head while making the shopping experience a more comfortable and enjoyable occasion.

A P&O 'brand wall' will give a flavour of the long and distinguished company heritage leading up to the 175th anniversary in 2012. A short film will be shown on the television screens depicting the history of P&O's people, ships and imagery. Elsewhere icons of Britain / icons of France screens on each ship will tell the story of each country through a series of well-chosen images. More evidence of the P&O tradition is found in the Club Lounge in the *Spirit of Britain* which features a Robert Lloyd painting of the ship (see page 118) in addition to the bell of the Falklands veteran *Norland* which during her career was operated by P&O North Sea Ferries on routes from Hull but which was sadly sent to the breakers yard in 2010.

SEATING AND EATING

In the two new ships, P&O have provided more seats than people and have recognised that everyone has a right to a view. In order to achieve this, the central seating areas in the food court have been raised so that even if sitting away from the outside of the ship, a view of the Channel can be won through the large panoramic windows. These raised areas can be shut off during quieter periods when fewer passengers are travelling. The aft bar has been designed to be closed off at quieter times without it being obvious to the customer, to maintain a better atmosphere and for maintenance. Seating areas are arranged in different 'nesting zones' featuring a variety of styles to suit every taste throughout the vessel for children, teenagers and couples, while maintaining the essential easy to clean perspective. Neither have the freight and coach drivers been neglected in P&O's bid to provide the ultimate ferries for the Dover-Calais route. The Routemasters Freight and Coach Club offers a food court, relaxation area, self-serve drinks, outside balcony, seat-back television screens and shower units.

The ships are as light and airy as it is possible to make them and on-board lighting reacts according to the light entering the ship from outside throughout the day and night.

It is recognised that dining styles have changed throughout the years and the new ships duly reflect this in the creation of a Carluccio's/ Café Rouge-style brasserie for those who wish to sample high-class cuisine. Meanwhile the Food Court contains refrigerators based on the Marks & Spencer motorway station/railway station concept for those who simply wish to 'grab and go'. This is sited in the centre of the ships and very much reflects the High Street experience with which many customers are familiar. The food offer is being developed for healthy and lighter options, improved bean to cup coffee and a quality fast food experience at High Street prices to appeal to all the customer segments.

The Club Class experience will be refreshed with a self-serve airline style snack proposition, outside private decking with upmarket furniture, whilst stewards will still be at hand to help the journey needs of customers.

Behind the scenes, increased efficiency is evident across the board. No fewer than five different propulsion systems were evaluated before four engines, two propellers and three bow thrusts were chosen to allow extensive manoeuvring in a reliable and fuel-efficient context. This is certainly assisted by the hydro-dynamically efficient hull while the ships' reduced fuel consumption will give lower CO_2 emissions. These state-of-the-art technology tools have been used for future proofing and the ships qualify for a Lloyd's Register Green Passport in addition to being the first to meet new Safe Return to Port Regulations.

The *Spirit of Britain* and *Spirit of France* replace the *Pride of Dover* and *Pride of Calais* which have reliably served the Dover-Calais route since 1987. Billed at that time as the 'Chunnel Beaters' the new ships offer double the freight capacity (a massive 3.5km of freight per sailing) with approximately the same fuel consumption but significantly lower engine emissions.

As P&O Ferries are happy to advise, "Sit back and relax".

chapter
seven

The ship the business wanted

by Mike Langley
Programme Manager

After 35 years' experience as a seagoing engineer, followed by another six ashore in various fleet management roles, it was with huge enthusiasm that I was privileged to become involved in the new-build project, initially as part of my role as Head of Technical Management and latterly full time as the Programme Manager.

In early 2006 the Executive Board approved a brief internal feasibility study into replacing the *Pride of Dover* and *Pride of Calais* with new tonnage. Previous work in 2003 had identified several options including fast craft, double-enders and the largest vessels for the Dover-Calais route. This decision coincided with the bi-annual Ro-Ro conference in Ghent, Belgium, and so I was despatched to hear presentations on the Canadian double-enders, efficient hull forms and hull design optimisation which all featured on the programme.

It was at this conference that I met Markku Kanerva for the first time. Little did I know that this was to be the starting point of a long and strong relationship for P&O Ferries and DeltaMarin.

After the conference I analysed the previous work reporting back to the Fleet Director, John Garner. The work was in turn reported back to the Executive Board and we were given the approval to progress to a full feasibility study. The next step was to research and interview prospective naval architect consultancy companies.

Historically with Three Quays Consultancy (an in-Group company) there would have been no selection process but following our change of shareholders to DP World, we were able to take a clean sheet of paper approach. We did, however, invite Three Quays and other leading consultants to present; this culminating in the appointment of DeltaMarin in February 2007 to assist us with a full feasibility study.

At this point I was seconded into the role of 'Programme Manager New Build'.

The first meeting was held in Channel House in Dover and included a visit to some of our Dover-Calais ships. It soon became apparent that these ships were going to be designed and built for the whole business, so the feasibility study moved forward with the involvement of IT, On-board Services, Freight and Tourist Marketing.

SMC were selected from a shortlist of renowned accommodation designers and were to be the lead designers supported by KKD, a retail designer with no previous marine experience. Together they would design the retail and adjacent seating areas, an arrangement that resulted in many challenges at the drawing approval stage.

The feasibility study was conducted at a high level with a small team of Directors, Senior Managers, Lloyd's Register, and MCA. The study defined the main dimensions and capacities, preliminary general/machinery arrangements, lightweight, hull form and hydrostatics, capacities and sub-division, loading conditions and stability, powering and finally provided an estimation of build cost.

Once the feasibility study was accepted by the Board, we moved on to a full outline specification and a larger team was built up to include Captains, Chief Engineers, Electrical Technical Officers, Technical Managers and On-board Services Managers.

On-board Services contributed with a small team headed up by

The last rays of the setting sun catch the **Spirit of Britain**'s starboard side as she is coaxed towards her fitting out berth at Rauma. *(John Hendy)*

Andy Mortimer to determine the best passenger accommodation layout, incorporating good back of house support arrangements. The marketing team contributed to the accommodation and car deck layouts and capacities.

We also went out to all the sea and shore staff canvassing their opinions and we received an overwhelming response which optimised the design for maximum operational and passenger benefit.

Finance assigned an analyst, Montu Modi, to support me, an arrangement that worked very well, and Montu was suitably impressed when he witnessed the float out of Hull 1367 and her arrival in Dover as the *Spirit of Britain*.

The Masters carried out some initial manoeuvring with Safety At Sea in Glasgow to investigate and establish the size of ship which could be operated within the existing port infrastructure and at what wind speeds.

Towards the end of this process I was able to integrate Steve Morant, ex-P&O Cruises and ex-P&O Ferries (Portsmouth), into the team as Project Manager. Steve had recent new-build experience with P&O Cruises, and was able to assist with the final design stages and eventually be located in Rauma in charge of the Quality Inspection Team. His administration skills and determination to get things right was to be reflected in the final product.

The specification produced was very comprehensive, including a

2,000-passenger capacity. The passenger accommodation comprised of two decks covering the whole length of the ship, with escalators and outside glass lifts. After inviting expressions of interest, the full specifications were offered for tender. The tenders received indicated that the cost range fell outside our estimated range, so the specification was reduced to a 1,500-passenger capacity with reduced passenger areas and without the wished for escalators and outside lifts.

Once the revised tenders were received, the Board produced a shortlist of the main contenders and I personally visited those shipyards. Accompanied by the two shipbrokers, Jan Rasmussen (Trollship) and Totto Hartmann (Platou) together with the DeltaMarin naval architect, Toni, we embarked on a whistle stop tour of European and Far East shipyards. This whole process has to be one of the highlights of my career. To be given the responsibility to inspect the shipyards, clarify the specification and then report back to the New Build Steering Group, which at that time comprised of the CEO, CFO, Fleet, OBS, Marketing, Operations and Communications Directors, plus other senior managers from the business, was a privilege.

Each visit was followed up with a meeting at our shareholders' London office, sometimes with designated members of the new-build design team also attending. At the end of these meetings a risk reward analysis of the tenders was carried out and we short-listed further to three shipyards. Aker Shipyards, now STX Europe, was

The ship the business wanted

This image shows the lift which brings containers directly from the main vehicle Deck 3 (top) down to Deck 2 for unloading during a Channel crossing. This process, used earlier in the *P&OSL Canterbury*, greatly assists during turn round times at Dover. *(Miles Cowsill)*

chosen because of their early delivery opportunity, and their extensive ferry-building experience. Although I believe we could have built at the other shipyards, this would have required a larger project management team. The enthusiasm and attention to detail of the Koreans was very impressive and the openness and environment of the small Italian yard would have also made for a good experience.

Once the letter of intent was signed, there was a very extensive period where we had to agree an Aker contract specification together with the need to ensure that all our requirements were incorporated in this specification. We had previously investigated propulsion packages, the majority of the Short Sea fleet being propelled by Sulzer engines, and we enlisted some assistance from the North Sea Fleet Chief Engineers with Wartsila 46C experience, before approving the installed MAN package. As the MAN package was new for our fleet, and in particular the MAN Alpha propeller package, we insisted on them visiting the Short Sea fleet and witnessing the whole route operation from the coastguard station above the White Cliffs of Dover. This proved to be invaluable later in the project.

By the time we had finished this process we had restored the passenger number to a maximum of 2,000, although it took a longer process before this was included in the final General Arrangement, increasing to 1,750 and then finally 2,000 in 2010.

For the shipbuilding contract we proposed the BIMCO standard passenger ship contract format, having been to a BIMCO presentation

Waiting for the float out: the *Spirit of Britain*'s superstructure towers above the dock side at Rauma. *(John Hendy)*

in London some months earlier to learn about shipbuilding contracts. A Norwegian lawyer was engaged to draw up the contract, supported admirably by our in-house lawyer, Susan Kitchin, and aided on technical issues by myself.

The final contract was reviewed and approved by the Board and on 7th August 2008 the shipbuilding contract was signed. With the contract signed, my secondment became permanent and we now worked together with STX to jointly design and approve the final product, with monthly meetings and visits to manufacturers.

By 3rd March, STX were able to start production, and we started to put owner inspectors in place. It was felt that by using a mixture of local experienced inspectors from DeltaMarin and our own seconded sea staff, we could achieve a high standard of approval together with an operational and construction approval skill base. We supplemented this skills base by placing all our seconded sea staff, together with Steve and myself, on the Lloyd's Register new-build supervision training course.

As the project progressed to keel laying on 25th August 2009, more time was spent on production and less on design although several late changes on the passenger decks challenged STX and the design team but resulted in a better proposition at delivery.

As the inspection team completed production schedule inspections through the winter, I attended the yard for about one week every month. The rest of my time was spent consulting and reporting to the business on progress made and emerging issues.

Finally after a very long and very cold Finnish winter, Hull 1367 was floated out and the keel was laid of Hull 1368 amidst a real party atmosphere. This was a very proud moment for the New Build Inspection Team.

As the outfitting progressed at pace and sea trials loomed, the finished product soon emerged. Sea trials were conducted in extreme Finnish winter weather which arrived about six weeks ahead of normal just to challenge us. All attending were very impressed with the ship's sea-keeping performance and comfort ability and whilst we were all apprehensive of the full speed steering tests, we were suitably impressed by the way the ship handled. We positioned a table and two chairs in the premium restaurant as a test and were pleased to discover that they remained in position throughout the steering and manoeuvring trials.

Unfortunately the light draught of the ship and high open sea winds meant that we could not collate the necessary data to input into the simulation model to verify the 50-knot wind manoeuvring capability. This data will be collected when the vessel is in service and the simulation model updated.

As is usual in ship management we had some final challenges before the *Spirit of Britain* was able to depart Rauma for her delivery voyage, approximately four hours late. This proved to be real experience for the delivery crew encountering ice, icebreaker escorts, snow, fog, north easterly and south westerly gales.

Finally on a gloriously sunny January Sunday, the *Spirit of Britain*

The Engine Room control room. *(John Hendy)*

emerged from the English Channel into her home port of Dover, escorted by two Dover Harbour Board tugs displaying the traditional fire hose salute.

As a Dovorian born and bred, this was a very proud moment for me. Now, as I approach the end of my career I am content that we have delivered a ship to match the Short Sea ferry generation breaking *Pride of Dover* and *Pride of Calais* and I am confident that the *Spirit of Britain* will in turn be the next generation breaking vessel for the route.

The success of the project is due to the involvement, professionalism and dedication of all the staff who contributed to the design and operation and as Programme Manager I was privileged to co-ordinate and manage this project.

I would like to thank the Board of Directors for their confidence and support that they gave me, together with all the staff who contributed to this project. The result is the ship the business wanted.

Event	Date
RoRo Ghent	May 2006
Start feasibility study	January 2007
Complete feasibility study	6th June 2007
Outline spec	Oct 2007
Contract spec	Jan 2008
LOI (letter of intent)	June 2008
Contract	August 2008
Design	September 2008
Start of production	3rd March 2009
Keel Laying	25th August 2009
Float out	8th June 2010
Sea trials	23rd November 2010
Delivery	5th January 2011
Entry into service	21st January 2011

chapter
eight

A
new era of
passenger
travel

by John Garner

Fleet Director

During 2006, P&O Ferries had a strategic review of its future ship disposition and fleet requirements. This review indicated that against a backdrop of freight traffic growth and a high level of ongoing demand from tourist passengers, the Dover-Calais route would require new vessels in the near future. The two main drivers were the commercial demand for more space, particularly freight space, and an evaluation of the lifespan of the two existing sister vessels, *Pride of Dover* and *Pride of Calais*. We took a view that it would be advantageous to introduce new tonnage before the *Pride of Dover* and *Pride of Calais* were required to undergo their 25-year special surveys. At the same time, introducing new tonnage would allow us to keep pace with the more demanding SOLAS Regulations and the ever increasing volume of environmental regulations.

The two sister ships, *Pride of Dover* and *Pride of Calais*, had set a new reference standard or benchmark for cross-Channel ferry travel when they were introduced in 1987. Both ships have served the Dover-Calais route exceptionally well and our challenge was to determine the concept and design to build ships that would take us forward into the next era. In short, we needed to have the same vision for a 25-year period as the designers of the *Pride of Dover* and *Pride of Calais* had when they introduced those vessels.

The way we approached this was to use a cross-functional approach within our own company from the outset. We spent a lot of time in the early days carrying out demand studies of what our customers, both freight and tourist, required, likely future growth of both segments of the market, market share, frequency, port turnaround and reliability of the future vessels. We also opened up an e-mail address so that our seafaring colleagues who were operating the ships at the sharp end, and who knew all the intricate details of our vessels' operation, could e-mail their ideas, and we had a very good contribution from our colleagues at sea.

Early in 2007 we entered into a vital partnership with DeltaMarin of Finland as our naval architect lead design consultants. We had not built ships for Dover-Calais for a number of years, we had no in-house naval architects and we needed to understand the developing areas of technology and innovation. We consulted DeltaMarin on the basis of its successful track record and expertise gained from working on many cruise vessels and ro-ro passenger vessel projects.

We also selected an interior design specialist, London based SMC, to assist with the interior design. Two other partnerships that have proved vital are those with Lloyd's Register as our Classification Society and the Maritime & Coastguard Agency (MCA) as the UK Flag Administration, both of whom were selected based upon being our first choice. We had already had good experience of working closely with both organisations and solving technical challenges together.

We convened an early meeting with MCA, Lloyd's Register and DeltaMarin on 18th July 2007, where we explained our philosophy and rationale for the design and build of the new vessels, considered the use of the upcoming SOLAS 2009 Regulations with particular focus on damage stability and sought the MCA's view on the inclusion of the

Dressed overall, the **Spirit of Britain** edges up to berth 1 at Dover's Eastern Docks on the occasion of her delivery - 9th January 2011. *(John Hendy)*

Stockholm Regulations for water on deck and also their view on the use of lower holds. We put forward our intention to follow the successful 2003 Darwin project which resulted in the two passenger ro-ro ferries, *Pride of Kent* and *Pride of Canterbury*, using Marine Evacuation Systems (MES) as an equivalence to the SOLAS lifeboat requirements on the Dover-Calais route.

We also discussed in detail the upcoming IMO Safe Return to Port Regulations and innovations within the ship design, stating our intention for the vessel to meet the 'Green Passport' status which tracks all hazardous materials in the vessel from cradle to grave. We also considered the intervals between dry-docking of the vessel. As will be seen from this agenda, we were discussing the big areas for decision-making that would set the cornerstone for the foundations of the two new ships we would introduce for the future.

An interesting development was that as shipyards became aware of our intention to build, we had many approaches from them. The normal approach was to offer us a template provided by the yard such as a platform design from their previous experience. We had a very uncompromising view and a very clear opinion that our mission was to build the ships our business wanted, rather than the ships that were easier to produce at the shipyards. What this meant was that we took a 'bottom up' approach and with the help of DeltaMarin and the input of Lloyd's Register and the MCA we produced an outline specification and a preliminary General Arrangement plan by September 2007. We then went out to the shipyards which had expressed interest and having evaluated their responses, a total of 11 shipyards were visited. This evaluation process was not only technical in nature but also commercial, as we were accompanied by the brokers from Trollship and RS Platou to help us determine likely commercial pricing, structure and lead times for delivery. A shortlist of three yards was produced and we were very pleased to be able to select Aker Yards, now STX Europe based in Finland. However, we did not choose just the STX Group, we actually specified that we wanted to build in their specialist ferry site in Rauma, as we knew the management and staff of that yard had a lot of expertise in building state of the art ro-ro passenger ferries. Additionally the Rauma Yard has spearheaded new projects and as we would no doubt be pioneering in the areas of new regulations and optimisation of design, it was essential we had a shipyard at the forefront of technology and innovation.

Part of the process in determining which shipyard we would select was our requirement for quality and a short lead time, always mindful of the final price of the ships. Around the same time main engines were in short supply and STX were able to secure commitments for main engines. A letter of intent was signed in June 2008, followed by the signing of contracts in London on 7th August 2008. Steel

A new era of passenger travel

production commenced in March 2009, keel laying took place in August, the launch of the first vessel was in June 2010, and the delivery of the first vessel *Spirit of Britain* was as per plan on 5th January 2011 in Rauma.

Apart from the project and programme management arrangements we put in place with the shipyard, we also put in place a series of management level meetings which gave us a high level oversight and a forum to discuss the 'big ticket' items such as dates of delivery and production criteria linked to key milestones which are tied to stage payments. These management meetings proved to be invaluable.

One of the key requirements of the overall project was to be able to achieve significant economies of scale within the design concept of these new ferries. The end result can be seen in the *Spirit of Britain* and *Spirit of France*. Our desire was to have roughly the same level of operating costs and fuel consumption, deliver the same schedule and port turnaround as the ferries we are replacing, even though we will have more than double the payload of freight and tourist vehicles.

The 2,800 lane metres of freight is approximately double that of *Pride of Dover* and *Pride of Calais* and a new introduction to our Dover-Calais fleet in these vessels is that of a fixed third deck for tourist vehicles in addition to the two full height decks that can take freight and coaches. This results in having space for approximately 180 freight units as well as 195 tourist vehicles. The third deck has a headroom of 3.3m and the fixed ramps fore and aft adjoining Deck 7 and Deck 5 are 3.0m and 3.3m fore and aft respectively. This allows campers and caravans to access the third deck. Passenger capacity was finalised at 2,000 passengers.

Our vision was for these new ships to be as environmentally friendly as possible and to offer significant advances through fuel efficiency. This has been achieved by inclusion in the design brief which required a hydrodynamically efficient hull form developed by DeltaMarin and STX Finland using CFD techniques and developed through model tank tests at Marin in the Netherlands. Additionally we took a great deal of time in choosing a propulsion plant which will be able to deliver significant fuel savings.

The day before placing the contract with STX Finland, we finalised the choice of the propulsion plant. We chose MAN 7L48/60CR medium speed main engines providing a total propulsion of 30,400 kW. Our requirements were goal based and the contractual requirements were for the shipyard to produce a vessel which would deliver 22 knots in shallow water at 85% MCR and 15% sea margin. Due to the resistance in shallow water, this meant that the vessel would be capable of approximately 23 knots in deeper water. This specification came from our research into the depth of water specifically on the Dover-Calais route.

The main engines are designed to run on low sulphur fuel oil and meet the Tier II NOx emissions standards ahead of the mandatory, regulatory date. These engines are also fitted with common rail technology to enable better combustion through electronic ignition timing and thereby take away any traces of black carbon upon start-up of main engines.

Additionally, the new ships will have four MAN generators, two propeller shafts with shaft alternators that provide the three bow thrusts, each of 3MW power rating during manoeuvring.

We did consider other propulsion types, such as the Azimuth propulsers and a combination of diesel electric/mechanical systems. Finally we opted for the tried and tested option of four main engines driving two propellers with highly skewed propeller blades and Becker rudders with high levels of manoeuvrability. This propulsion layout in our view minimises the risk of machinery failure and provides inherent reliability as these vessels will carry out c3,500 voyages per annum.

In building ferries which have a lifespan of a minimum 25 years ahead of them, we had to consider the port infrastructure the vessel would be required to fit in Dover and Calais, both now and in the future. The challenge was to optimise the vessel size in relation to the existing port infrastructures and turning circles within the ports of Dover and Calais, as well as ensuring they would be able to fit in new infrastructure provided by these ports from 2015 onwards. This challenge led to significant discussions with both port authorities to ensure the berths and infrastructure could accommodate the new ships.

As a result of these, the vessels will fit berth 9 in Dover but berths 3 and 7 require lengthening to take the longer vessels. The new ships also have a wider beam of 30.8m as opposed to the standard width of 27.8m for Dover ferries. This wider beam has required an offset hull arrangement for the hull appendages such as the fenders so that the vessels can fit into the port linkspan arrangements to facilitate the rapid load/discharge of vehicles.

We also considered manoeuvrability to be a key criteria of these ferries which are the first to be designed able to manoeuvre under their own power in winds of 50 knots, which is just below the 55-knot threshold when Dover port is normally closed. This manoeuvring requirement sets a new higher threshold at which the vessels can manoeuvre without the assistance of tugs.

Part of our design criteria was also to develop these vessels with a new, enhanced level of passenger safety. Therefore at an early stage we took the significant decision to build the vessels to the new SOLAS 2009 requirements but also to the requirements of the Stockholm Agreement. This was a massive decision taken at the time without the comfort of the Flag states being able to confirm their view of whether the new regulations and what combination of them, would give the optimum level of safety. Our decision was vindicated a year later when the UK Maritime Coastguard Agency recommended building all new passenger ferries to SOLAS 2009 and the Stockholm Agreement.

We have also delivered an enhanced level of passenger safety as these will be the first passenger ferries in the world to comply with IMO's new Safe Return to Port requirements ahead of the compliance date. The development work for Safe Return to Port was done

Face to face with the *Spirit of Britain*. [John Hendy]

A new era of passenger travel

through brainstorming sessions held between ourselves, MCA, Lloyd's Register, DeltaMarin and STX Finland. Part of the solution was for us to have Lloyd's Register PSMR* Class notation which is the highest level for propulsion, steering and machinery redundancy. Again this was a pioneering aspect as, for instance, the four main engines are separated and offset in separate engine rooms. To ensure complete watertight integrity the port tailshaft is protected by a steel watertight tunnel. This ensures the requirements of Safe Return to Port are fully met.

The safety consideration of having all Marine Escape Systems only as an equivalence to the SOLAS lifeboat requirements was one which we were comfortable with having operated the *Pride of Kent* and *Pride of Canterbury* in that mode since 2003. The experience we have gained on these two ships indicated to us on safety grounds alone that dry-shod marine escape units are preferable as life-saving appliances to the open lifeboats prescribed under SOLAS.

A significant operational challenge which we will face during times of peak customer demand such as the summer holiday period is the load and discharge of full loads in and out of port in the allocated time of 45-50 minutes. Some new technical features have been incorporated to help achieve this such as faster opening and closing of cargo doors and a revised layout for the supply of stores to the vessel. The storing arrangements allow a trailer unit to drive on to a lift platform on the main vehicle deck and then be lowered into the watertight stores area and the cargo lid closed on the main vehicle deck. This allows the trailer unit full of ship's stores to be taken on voyage from Dover-Calais and back, during which time the stores can be discharged directly into the stores area on Deck 2.

Additionally we carried out simulations for the loading/discharging of freight vehicles and passenger cars and supplemented these with a port turnaround project convened in house with staff involved from all pertinent areas. This project has been successful in identifying areas of time reduction during the port turnaround. A design feature is that the freight lanes are of 3.2m lane width, wider than many other ro-pax ships, and this will help facilitate turnaround times and reduce the risk of damage to both ship and vehicles.

Turning to the passenger decks, one of the key meetings with STX Finland determined that the standard of the fixtures, fittings and upholstery arrangements of the passenger decks was set by confirming the Tallink cruise ferry *Galaxy* as the reference ship. This was absolutely key in setting the standard and our interior designers, SMC, worked very closely both with our colleagues internally and STX Finland to produce the final result. The results, which can be witnessed in the passenger decks of the *Spirit of Britain* and *Spirit of France*, set in our mind a new reference and benchmark for the standard of passenger ferries on the Channel. The layout of the passenger decks is in accordance with the demands that we will gain from our customers, whether it be the family lounge, free flow restaurant, premium dining restaurant, freight drivers area or Club Lounge. Outside passenger decks have also been provided, which

together with the very large picture-sized windows give excellent views externally for all of the passengers.

A key operational feature is that the back-of-house areas such as the galleys, serveries etc have been designed for ease of operation to support delivery of a high-quality product to the customers.

Operational flexibility has been built into the passenger decks as a design feature. This innovation through design rather than retro-fit allows P&O Ferries to take certain areas of the passenger decks out of service in a very discreet way when passenger numbers are low. This means that we can still provide a quality passenger experience but also facilitate flexible manning of the passenger decks which is matched to the differing levels of passenger demand throughout the year.

The various energy and labour saving devices and arrangements installed throughout the ships are a result of input from our colleagues both ashore and afloat. Their contributions have been utilised within the complete design of the vessels to optimise the product and delivery that we will give to our customers. As such this has been a cross-functional project from the beginning and we have drawn from the immense knowledge of our colleagues working at the sharp end on board our ferries.

In closing, I would like to thank all those who have made a contribution to these vessels, without which we would not have ended up with the two new quality vessels *Spirit of Britain* and *Spirit of France*. A key factor in delivering this success has been to build partnerships both internally within the company and externally with those already mentioned above, so that the completed vessels provide an integrated transport solution to our customers for what I am sure will herald a new era of passenger ferry travel.

Looking astern on the approach to Calais on the *Spirit of Britain*'s maiden voyage - 21st January 2011. *(John Hendy)*

Always moving forward

The Port of Dover is Europe's busiest ferry port handling in excess of 5 million vehicles annually and over 15 million passengers, providing state-of-the-art facilities for a wide range of services in the ferry, cargo, cruise and marina markets.

Forward thinking expertise and investments in new technologies has ensured that the Port of Dover remains positioned as a leading port infrastructure provider, that strives to continually move forward.

PORT OF
DOVER
BRITAIN'S
FAVOURITE PORT

www.doverport.co.uk

99

nine

Factors that guided the development of the Spirit of Britain

by Captain David Miller

Captain of the *Spirit of Britain*

To better understand the Spirit of Britain, *it may be of interest to consider the factors that guided her development and the ship that evolved.*

On several occasions in recent years P&O have investigated new tonnage for the Dover-Calais route. The last occasion was in 2002 when the decision was made not to build but to covert the freight ships *European Pathway* and *European Highway* into the *Pride of Canterbury* and *Pride of Kent*. With the *Pride of Dover* and *Pride of Calais* approaching their 25th anniversary, new tonnage was a project whose time had come. The *Pride of Dover* and *Pride of Calais* have proved superb Company servants delivering ten crossings a day, day in day out, year in year out with almost metronome regularity. How were P&O to replace ships which had set the standard for cross-Channel travel for nearly a quarter of a century?

In July 2006, our Fleet Director John Garner travelled on the *Pride of Kent* and in discussion posed the question of what was the largest ship that could be operated on the Dover-Calais route. His requirement was a ship able to operate within the limitations of existing infrastructure but also able to make the most of the opportunities afforded by future infrastructure. He asked not for a full report but a one-page briefing paper. What started as a piece of A4 paper has become a 48,000-ton ship.

Calais has plans for a new port to the east of the existing harbour and Dover is also considering a second terminal adjacent to the old Hover port. However, as the new ships were required before either development was scheduled for completion, they had to fit current facilities. The critical factor in the existing ports is the size of the swinging basin in Calais and this determined the length of the ship.

With the length defined at 210 metres, her beam was an interesting consideration. Existing berths in both ports are designed for ships of between 28.3 to 28.5 metres but this beam does not optimise the carrying capability of a 210-metre ship. Any increase in beam had to be in freight lane increments of 3.2 metres and one additional lane would add 26 freight vehicles to the ship's capacity. But how do you get a 31.4-metre wide ship into a 28.3-metre wide berth? The solution is novel but effective and is based on the fact that all ships are stern to in Dover and bow to in Calais. All Calais berths are starboard side to and therefore the bow ramps have been offset to starboard. The most suitable berths in Dover are port side to so the stern ramps have been offset to port. The flexibility of this solution is that in an emergency the ship will also fit stern to in Calais and bow to in Dover.

With the footprint for the new Dover-Calais-Max ferry established, the question was what sort of ship should she be? The Directors gave the following clear brief:

She should fit the operational profile of the existing fleet and be able to maintain the service in the most severe weather

She should be innovative and embrace all expected legislation

She should be able to cope with increases in the weight of road vehicles during her life.

She should be fuel efficient and have minimum impact on the environment. She should exceed the expectation of our customers

WHAT SORT OF SHIP IS THE SPIRIT OF BRITAIN?

The *Spirit of Britain* brings a new level of sea keeping to the Short Sea Route. We built a 26-foot model of the ship and ran it in a test tank to optimise comfort in rough weather. The outcome predicted a 25% improvement in heavy seas and on the delivery voyage from Rauma we verified this. On passage we experienced gales from all directions but the ship proceeded serenely on towards Dover without slamming or vibration. Our crew are no strangers to rough weather and even they are surprised by the smoothness of the ride. Many passengers look at the weather forecast before their ferry crossing but on the *Spirit of Britain* we know they will be delighted by the ride.

Maintaining the schedule in all weathers is not just about sea keeping but also includes the ability to move such a large ship into and out of harbour. We set the threshold of manoeuvring in 50 knots of wind which is a considerable challenge for a ship with over 5,000 square metres of windage. To determine the size of the rudders, propellers and thrusters we made extensive use of ship-handling simulators. From this model testing we concluded we needed 9 mega watts of bow thrust and twin high lift rudders of 23.4 square metres each. Thrusters of this size are the largest STX has ever installed in a ferry and are even more powerful than the main engine power of the

Looking astern from the port bridge wing. *(John Hendy)*

Lion, P&O's first Dover ferry!

In addition to the ship-handling simulations we also made extensive use of computers to optimise the stability of the ship. Working with Strathclyde University we have developed the *Spirit of Britain* in accordance with the latest 'Probabilistic' stability rules and she is one of the first ships in the world to meet this stringent requirement.

This is not the only ground-breaking feature of her design as she is also the world's first passenger ship to be built to the principles of 'Safe Return to Port' (SRtP is based on the fact that the ship is her own best lifeboat). In the event of a fire, we quarantine the space and make our way back to port. This is a very challenging criteria that severely challenged everyone in the design and development team. It has been well worth all the brain storming that ensued because it takes safety and decision-support to a totally new level.

The travelling public have a historic view of cross-Channel travel. However, much has changed in recent years and the *Spirit of Britain*'s passenger facilities are of cruise ship standards. The ship was built by STX Europe, who have recently completed the two largest

With the port side bridge combinators on the left of this view, windows on the deck's floor allow the Captain a bird's eye view of the ship's side during the berthing procedure. *(John Hendy)*

Factors that guided the development of the Spirit of Britain

The *Spirit of Britain*'s triple bow-thrusters are seen at work as she manoeuvres in Dover Harbour. *(John Hendy)*

passenger ships in the world. The shipbuilder's experience is clearly reflected in our interior design which is contemporary and welcoming with extensive use of glass, stone and stainless steel.

The cruise ship analogy also extends to noise and vibration which has been reduced to luxury passenger ship levels. STX have paid particular attention to the design of the structure and the *Spirit of Britain* is much quieter both at sea and when manoeuvring. This is one of the key attributes of the ship and on sea trials many of us found it difficult to believe how quiet she was when running at full power making 24 knots into a Baltic gale.

In the design and development of STX yard number 1367, we have strived to build a ground-breaking ship that significantly changes the perception of cross-Channel travel. Think of what high-speed trains have done for rail travel and what jumbo jets have done for air travel. We hope that the *Spirit of Britain* combines the best of both these transport milestones delivering a fast reliable service with a carrying capacity twice that of the ship she replaces.

Replacing the *Pride of Dover* is a very hard act to follow but we have a superb ship and a dedicated crew. As we embark on the maiden voyage it is a good time to reflect on all we have achieved over the past four years and look forward to many years of trouble-free service. I feel we have met the Directors' design brief and hope our passengers really enjoy the experience. We seek to make the *Spirit of Britain* the customers' preferred cross-Channel ferry and a 21st century alternative to a 20th century train set.

Looking across the full width of the ship's bridge. *(John Hendy)*

Captain David Miller is at the combinators as he brings his ship towards berth 1 at the conclusion of her delivery voyage. *(John Hendy)*

The *Spirit of Britain* bow in at Dover's berth 1 on the day before her maiden voyage. *(Miles Cowsill)*

Raising the benchmark for the environment

by Steve Stagg
Chief Engineering Officer

Raising the benchmark for the environment

A Chief Engineer and a passion for environmental concerns may appear at first to be strange bedfellows. How can someone who works in an industry where individual vessels daily use considerable quantities of fossil fuel possibly be interested in the long-term health of our planet?

Although large amounts of non-renewable energy are consumed, shipping is arguably (ton for ton) the most efficient form of mainstream transport and therefore arguably the greenest. A small efficiency improvement of a few per cent can mean a significant saving. It then starts to make sense that pursuing this chosen career path can complement one's own environmental standards.

The brief from the Directors of P&O Ferries was simple. Design and construct a class of vessel that would carry twice the payload using the same amount of energy. It would take the best designers, engineers and technicians in Europe to fulfill this ambitious vision.

Key to the implementation was to design a ground-breaking hull form, use cutting edge energy-saving technologies and to squeeze every last possible joule of energy from the precious fuel. Four computers precisely control and monitor the fuel injected into the ship's main engines. Accuracy is measured in milliseconds and millilitres to ensure near complete combustion.

At over 300 degrees, exhaust gases from the main engines are still hot enough to generate steam that in turn provides an abundance of hot water and heating for the accommodation. Cooling water for the main engines is used to boil sea water under vacuum in evaporators. Although not of high enough quality to drink, this provides fresh water for washing down decks and topping up ship's systems.

Attention to detail ensures that electrical consumption is kept as low as possible. Major pumps and fans are frequency controlled, varying speed according to demand. Lighting using energy-saving lamps and LEDs has been used extensively throughout. In addition, sensors and computers automatically reduce indoor lighting output depending on light entering from windows. Areas not in use have lighting dimmed and ventilation levels reduced.

Seawater is used for passenger toilet flushing and this is then processed on board over a 24-hour period. Chlorinated, then de-chlorinated before passing overboard, we return it to the sea in a cleaner state than when it was drawn into the vessel.

Finally the largest energy saving is possibly the propulsion system itself. The speed and pitch of the two propellers is finely adjustable; load computers constantly alter settings to compensate for wind and current whilst delivering the desired speed set by the Master to achieve a timely arrival.

None of this would be possible without constant monitoring. A small team of technical staff analyse inputs from over 6,000 sensors around the vessel. The results are then used to optimise machinery and equipment for maximum efficiency.

The benchmark has been raised not only in terms of comfort but also for those amongst us looking for an environmentally responsible form of transport. Look no further than the new 'Spirit' class of vessels for your next crossing.

Saluting the *Spirit of Britain*: the twin Dover Harbour Board tugs welcome the port's newest ship. *(John Hendy)*

eleven

From AKER Yards to STX Europe

STX Europe ASA comprises 15 shipyards in Brazil, Finland, France, Norway, Romania, and Vietnam. In addition STX Europe has three partly owned yards in Germany and Ukraine. Formerly known as Aker Yards, the company changed its name to STX Europe during autumn 2008, after it was acquired by STX, an industrial business group based in South Korea.

STX Europe's operations are organised around the three business areas: Cruise & Ferries, Offshore & Specialised Vessels and what are termed, Other Operations. The group's head office is located in Oslo, Norway. The company employs some 16,000 people who incorporate 270 years of shipbuilding history and centuries of maritime expertise, experience and culture. With numerous locations around the world, STX Europe aims to provide the right combination of capabilities, capacity and market proximity to meet the needs of diverse customers with cost-competitive solutions.

STX Europe and its subsidiaries have gained a reputation as a preferred shipbuilder for many of the world's most successful ship owners and have built this position on a strategy of going beyond just building ships. The company is continually striving to develop new designs, introducing features and technologies which provide even higher performance and thus generate more value for their clients. To be able to develop new and improved concepts, they are constantly out among their clients' customers, researching trends and new business opportunities. Similarly, they are constantly striving for step change improvements in project execution, productivity and cost efficiency, by leveraging best practice from throughout the STX Business Group.

CRUISE SHIPS AND FERRIES

The 15 largest cruise ships in the world were or are currently being built by STX Europe yards. Their customers are the largest, most professional and most popular cruise lines in the world. STX Europe is also one of Europe's top three ferry builders. Building passenger ships goes beyond traditional shipbuilding skills, in that the innovation, quality and workmanship of components installed in the ships' hotels and other passenger areas are crucial to the vessels' eventual market success. The cruise ship designers, engineers and construction workers at the yards in France and Finland possess deep industry expertise and have provided valuable contributions to the global cruise industry's success in recent years.

OFFSHORE AND OTHER SPECIALISED VESSELS

More than four decades of oil and gas extraction in the North Sea has provided impetus to the development of highly specialised technology – and anchorage to a cluster of providers of products and services to the industry. From its Norway base, STX Europe has emerged as a leading player in the global market for purpose-built offshore service vessels. The vessels are primarily built at the yards in Norway, Romania, Brazil and Vietnam. The Romanian yards mainly produce vessel hulls, which are transported to Norway for

Viking Line's *Viking XPRS* operates between Helsinki and Tallinn and displays many of her builder's hallmarks. *(STX)*

final outfitting. In Vietnam and Brazil, the yards produce complete offshore vessels, mainly for operation in local markets. STX Europe's yards in Norway, Finland and France also build complex and sophisticated vessels for a number of other specialised segments, such as polar vessels, fishing vessels, naval craft, research vessels and coastguard vessels. STX Europe has unparalleled knowledge of ice technology, and has built 60% of the world's icebreakers.

OTHER OPERATIONS

Other Operations comprises units for development and sale of Arctic technologies, LNG technologies, and other solutions. STX

Europe is widely recognised as globally leading in Arctic technology expertise, with its own ice and Arctic laboratory in Finland. Other Operations also includes the shipyard in Florø, Norway, which is currently building a series of six chemical tankers. Both the LNG and the Arctic technology teams work closely with other units in the group, but also pursue stand-alone market opportunities. All of the business areas also provide solutions for efficient logistics, maritime environmental precaution and reduced energy consumption and operational costs.

RAUMA and STX FINLAND

STX Finland operates three yards which employ some 3,800

The cruise ferry *Baltic Princess* was built by STX Helsinki although most of the hull came from the company's St Nazaire yard. *(Miles Cowsill)*

Color Line's luxurious *Color Fantasy* and *Color Magic* operate between Oslo and Kiel and were built by STX at Turku. *(STX)*

The *Spirit of Britain* heads for Calais on a bright February day. This view shows a full deck of freight on Deck 5, the Dover 'skywalk' and car deck on Deck 7 in addition to the outside passenger areas (including Routemasters) on Decks 8 and 9. *(FotoFlite)*

From AKER Yards to STX Europe

Color Line's **Superspeed 1** and **Superspeed 2** (pictured) are 27 knot ferries employed on the Kristiansand and Larvik (Norway) to Hirtshals (Denmark) routes. Both came from the Rauma yard in 2008. *(STX)*

personnel – in Helsinki, Turku and Rauma. The Helsinki yard specialises in ice-breaking and ice-going offshore and Arctic vessels as well as car-passenger ferries. At Turku, the construction of large cruise ships is a speciality while at Rauma, ferries, icebreakers, naval vessels and smaller cruise ships are built.

The Rauma yard boasts a building dock that measures 260 metres x 85 metres in which both the *Spirit of Britain* and *Spirit of France* were constructed.

In recent years, amongst other vessels, the Rauma yard has built both the ferries *Baltic Queen* (for the Stockholm-Tallinn route) and the *Spirit of Britain*'s reference ship *Galaxy* (originally for the Tallinn-Helsinki link but presently running between Turku and Stockholm).

During 2009 the yard was presented with an extremely challenging job converting a vehicle ferry into an expedition cruise ship named *Expedition*. This was none other than the elderly 1972-built *Alandsfarjan* which in an earlier life had been one of the original P&O Normandy Ferries running on the Dover-Boulogne service as the *nf Tiger*. With her original capacity of 1,500 passengers and 200 cars/20 lorries, the ship very much belonged to an earlier age and would most certainly be dwarfed by the *Spirit of Britain* but STX's expertise was able to insert steel structures for new cabins on what had once been her car decks. Today's 120 passengers will have little idea of the ship's heritage as they explore the land of the polar bear or head for the Antarctic in the wake of Ernest Shackleton.

The **Birka Paradise** was built at Rauma in 2004 for the service between Stockholm and the Aland Islands. *(STX)*

Undergoing conversion from car ferry to specialist cruise ship at Rauma, the **Expedition** was once P&O Ferries' **nf Tiger**. *(STX)*

THE CHANNEL'S
GREATEST
ONES

STX Europe delivers two new vessels for P&O Ferries. The Spirit of Britain, followed by it's sister ship Spirit of France, will be the largest ferries operating on the English Channel. In addition to space for approximately 180 freight trucks and 195 passenger cars, the Spirit of Britain provides a safe and environmentally friendly passage for 2000 passengers. Both vessels are built in STX Finland Rauma shipyard.

www.stxeurope.com

stx Finland
member of STX Europe

chapter
twelve

Spirit of Britain from float out to delivery

A brilliantly warm and sunny day in Rauma was the appropriate occasion and a memorable setting for the float out of the *Spirit of Britain*.

A small group of UK-based journalists gathered at the STX yard at 08.30 for a guided visit to the new ship. In contrast to the weather outside, the internal passenger spaces presented a bleak sight with cavernous hectares of unpainted steel interrupted by kilometres of draped wire. The banging of hammers and the resonant and intermittent scream and whirr of drills echoed around the ship's vast empty spaces as our guides fought to explain the relevance of each particular area. To the uninitiated, the scene was one of organised chaos and indeed, it was quite remarkable that within the short space of seven months, the ship was at sea and heading for Dover.

Then at 11.00, with the local brass band playing on the adjacent quayside, the five huge valves were opened in the dry dock's protective gate behind which the *Spirit of Britain* lay perched on her blocks. Balloons were then released into the clear blue sky as thousands of gallons of water rushed in to float the ship.

The occasion had been preceded by the *Spirit of France*'s time-honoured keel-laying 'lucky coin ceremony' which is an ancient tradition designed to bring good fortune to the new ship. The vessel's first building block is lowered on top of the keel-block on which the coins are placed. The morning's work accomplished, lunch was taken in a nearby restaurant.

This was followed by a press conference at which P&O Ferries' CEO Helen Deeble divulged that had the order for the new twins been made two or three months later, due to the state of the global recession it may have been difficult to raise the necessary finance to build them. Freight on the Dover-Calais service was down by 15% and P&O were expecting another couple of tough years although one bright spot in the economic gloom indicated that tourist traffic was holding up. The company have taken a long-term view in which they will see market recovery over time thereby placing P&O Ferries in the best position to capitalise on the eventual economic upsurge.

The new ships have been designed for a life of at least 25 years and incorporate a number of world firsts, particularly in terms of hull design and in being the first ferries to comply with the new Safe Return to Port regulations.

Helen Deeble was followed to the microphone by the Chairman of P&O Ferries, Robert Woods. He was delighted that STX Europe were building "the best ferries that money can buy" and believed that they would become the most recognisable ships in the English Channel. He believed that people would marvel at their sheer size, the brilliance of their design, the luxurious nature of their facilities and their environmental credentials. The ships embodied everything that P&O holds dear such as quality and innovation.

By late afternoon the *Spirit of Britain* was afloat and Captain

Miller and the STX team were busy down below checking the integrity of the hull; the painstaking but vital process that takes place following every ship launch.

As the sun began to sink in the Baltic Sea and the levels of water both inside and outside the dock finally reached equilibrium, tugs assisted in the delicate task of easing the gate away from the dock's entrance. Lines were then attached to the *Spirit of Britain* and inch-by-inch, the ship was gently eased away from her birthplace, the dead ship proceeding so slowly that at times her movement appeared almost imperceptible.

Once clear of the dock, the new ferry was turned in the outer harbour and nursed back to the waiting fitting out berth. The lock gate was duly reinstated, the dock pumped dry to allow work on the *Spirit of France* to begin in earnest.

THE JOURNEY HOME - 5th-9th January 2011

The *Spirit of Britain* left Rauma for four days of trials in the Gulf of Bothnia at 10.00 on 23rd November. Temperatures were sub-zero and the ship encountered gale force winds during this period but a delighted Captain Miller reported that his ship had performed excellently.

Assisted by the tug *Polaris* and led by the 10,000-ton icebreaker *Nordica* and a local pilot vessel, the *Spirit of Britain* commenced her journey to Dover during the late afternoon of Wednesday 5th

January. In the UK, the last month of 2010 proved to be the coldest December since records began and Scandinavia's records also tumbled with the deepest snow since 1915 in the south of the country. There was a wind chill factor on the day of departure of -30 degrees centigrade with the sea frozen to a depth of about a metre. Previously, the Finnish flag had been lowered and the Red Ensign raised as the vessel was officially handed over to her new owners.

During her first night at sea, the icebreaker preceded the 'Spirit' across the Gulf of Bothnia to the Swedish side, passing west of the Aland archipelago. Headwinds of 40 knots were then encountered travelling southwards into the Baltic Sea at about 17 knots where later in the day she passed between the islands of Gotland and Oland. At 23.00 on the night of Thursday 6th January, the ship was heading SW and passing through the Bornholmsgat between the Danish island of Bornholm and Skane at the southern tip of Sweden.

Rather than take the narrow and congested passage through the Sound between Copenhagen and Malmo, the ship continued by heading south of the Danish island of Lolland, crossing the ferry route between Gedser and Rostock and later passing through the Fehmarn Belt between Rodby and Puttgarden where a fixed link is due to open by 2018. Another change of course then took the 'Spirit' northwards between the islands of Lolland and Langeland, through the Langeland Belt and across the Tars-Spodsbjerg ferry route.

She was now following the path of the Kiel to Oslo and

A post trials view of the **Spirit of Britain** at Rauma. With the sea a metre thick, a powerful icebreaker was called in to release her from Finland's winter grasp. *(STX)*

Spirit of Britain from float out to delivery

The start of a new era as the low winter sun catches the **Spirit of Britain** entering Dover Harbour for the first time on 9th January 2011. *(Brian Powell)*

Gothenburg overnight crossings into the Storebelt and just before 10.00 on the morning of Friday 7th January, she slipped under the impressive Great Belt bridge linking the Danish islands of Funen and Zealand between the once busy ferry ports of Nyborg and Korsor. It was then into the Samso Belt and across the ferry routes linking Arhus and Ebeltoft with Kalundborg and the port of Sjaellands Odde at the end of its long, low peninsula. Once past Grenaa, where the pilot was dropped during the early afternoon, the wide waters of the Kattegat were entered, the ship spending much of the afternoon and early evening testing new software south of the island of Anholt.

Eastwards of Anholt and then Laeso, she then picked up speed to 23.5 knots after which she crossed the track of the Frederikshavn-Gothenburg link before the course was set to round the Skaw at the northern tip of Denmark which was duly accomplished shortly before 22.00. The 'Spirit' was now sailing into the Skagerrak and crossed the Hirtshals-Kristiansand passage before the final homeward stretch, southwards through the North Sea.

This proved to be a more leisurely affair cruising at about 12 knots ready to arrive in Dover at the appointed hour of 11.00 on Sunday 9th January. The ship made such good time that by 04.30 she had slowed right down off the Goodwin Sands testing some more recently installed software. The weather at Dover on the previous two days had been dreadful with low cloud, rain, fog and gale force gusts and yet the sun rose on Sunday 9th January with

clear visibility and a bright blue sky with a fresh breeze which brought viewers out in their hundreds to witness the arrival of the English Channel's newest and largest ferry. To honour the occasion, the rest of the P&O fleet and the local tugs were dressed overall in readiness for the 'Spirit's' arrival.

The ship edged ever closer to the Eastern Entrance of Dover Harbour and, after waiting for incoming ferries to berth, she followed the freighter *European Seaway* towards her destination. Escorted by the twin Dover Harbour Board tugs shooting jets of water from their fire hoses high into the blue morning sky, the *Spirit of Britain* finally entered the harbour at 11.08 and crossed the bay towards the Prince of Wales Pier before swinging and heading for number 1 berth on the Eastern Arm. At 11.35 she was safely secured.

INTO SERVICE - 21st January

During the next 11 days a rigorous period of crew familiarisation and port-fit trails was carried out at both Dover and Calais as the ship was made ready for her maiden commercial voyage.

During this time a problem was experienced at Calais' berth 8, the preferred berth in the French port. As the entire port is built on a sand base with no foundations possible on solid bedrock, the Calais port authorities had been concerned that the extra size and weight of the new ship could cause structural problems to the berth if, at any time, heavier than usual contact was made. In order to

Spirit of Britain from float out to delivery

Leaving Calais on her first commercial crossing to Dover, the **Spirit of Britain** shows the port a clean pair of heels. *(Miles Cowsill)*

offset any problems, additional fendering was therefore added to berth 8 which effectively moved the docked ship further away from the cradle in which she nests when bow in at the port. During trials at low water, it was therefore seen that these berth modifications made it desirable to extend the *Spirit of Britain*'s twin freight decks by 300 mm (Deck 5) and 150 mm (Deck 3) in order to allow a wider area for the linkspans to rest. Accordingly, the ship was sent to ARNO at Dunkirk for the work to be carried out over a 48-hour period from the evening of 24th January. Previously, the Dover 'skywalk' – the passenger footway at the ship's stern – had been extended by one metre to allow a more comfortable fit with the port's shore facilities. At Dover the ship's preferred berth is number 9 – the western most berth – with 7 and 6 being used as a

contingency when this is not available.

Such minor port-fit modifications are not unusual in the ferry industry and give a good indication of how tough pre-service tests and trials actually prove to be. The impending visit to Dunkirk did not delay the ship's maiden voyage celebrations which duly took place from Dover's berth 6 to Calais' berth 9 at 09.20 on the morning of Friday 21st January. Dressed overall and with a proud Captain David Miller in command, the *Spirit of Britain* left Dover dead on time and was feted by the local press and media as she crossed the Dover Strait for the first time with fare-paying passengers. Although other shipping movements briefly delayed her entry into Calais, the *Spirit of Britain* made excellent time and was off the port within an hour of leaving Dover.

Into service: the **Spirit of Britain** swings off her berth on her early afternoon arrival at Dover on 2nd February. *(John Hendy)*

Robert G. Lloyd. 2010.

A reproduction of Robert Lloyd's painting showing the *Spirit of Britain* and *Pride of Calais* in Dover Harbour. It was presented to the ship by the artist and John Hendy & Miles Cowsill of Ferry Publications and hangs in the Club Lounge.

Spirit of France

During the float out of the *Spirit of Britain* and keel laying of the *Spirit of France*, the opportunity was taken to tour the STX yard around which many building blocks for the second ship were on view.

Right: A bow section, showing one of the three bow-thrust apertures, awaits its move to the dry dock. *(Miles Cowsill)*

Top left: The ship's bridge was already glazed but lacked its bridge wings which rested in a nearby shed. *(John Hendy)*

Left: More passenger modules await lifting in the STX yard. *(John Hendy)*

Above: The forward passenger decks with the Food Court (top row of windows) and Family Lounge (below). *(John Hendy)*

Top: Working continued on the *Spirit of France* throughout the colder than usual Finnish winter. The bridge module complete with wings is now positioned. *(STX)*

Below: At the after end of the *Spirit of France*, work carries on apace across her snow-covered decks. *(STX)*

All you need to know about the Spirit of Britain

It's only when you compare the *Spirit of Britain* with other familiar landmarks that you really begin to appreciate her size.

Big Ben	96 metres
Top of Dover Castle above sea	144 metres
Canterbury Cathedral length	157 metres
The London 'gherkin'	195 metres
Spirit of Britain	**213 metres**
Canada Tower at Canary Wharf	246 metres

SPIRIT OF BRITAIN

Specification

Builders	STX Rauma, Finland
Yard Number	1367
Official number	917019
IMO number	9524231
Call sign	2DXD4
Cost	£157 million (180 million Euro)
Port of registry	Dover
Length overall	212.97 metres (692 ft)
Length between perpendiculars	197.90 metres
Breadth moulded	30.8 metres (100 ft)
Breadth max over fenders	31.427 metres
Max draught moulded	6.70 metres
Max draught from bottom of keel	6.715 metres

The *Spirit of Britain* approaching her preferred berth 9 in Dover Harbour on 8th February 2011. *(John Hendy)*

Nearing Dover on her delivery voyage, this view gives a good impression of her outside decks including the helipad behind the bridge. *(Brian Powell)*

Design draught moulded	6.55 metres
Design draught from bottom of keel	6.565 metres
Depth moulded to Deck 3	9.71 metres
Depth moulded to Deck 5	15.50 metres
Gross tonnage	47,592
Net tonnage	14,277
Deadweight	9,188 tons
Number of decks	12
Passengers	2,000
Truck lane metres	2,746 (approx 170 trucks) on Decks 3 & 5
Additional car lane metres	1,000 (approx 195 cars) on Deck 7
Lane width	3.2 metres
Propulsion	4 x MAN 7L48/60CR main engines, each 7,600kW (de-rated from 8,050 kW) 500 rpm. Two main engines are connected together to one CP propeller type Alpha. 4 x auxiliary engines type MAN 7L21/31 each 1,424 kW, 1,000 rpm, 415V/50Hz
Output	30,400 kW (40,767 hp)
Speed	22 knots
Contract signed	7th August 2008
Start of production	3rd March 2009
Keel laid	25th August 2009
Launch	6th June 2010
Left the yard	5th January 2011
Arrived Dover	9th January 2011
Maiden Voyage	21st January 2011
Naming ceremony	24th March 2011
Classification Society	Lloyd's Register
Class marks and notations	LR+100A1, RoRo passenger ship +LMC, UMS, IWS, EP, PSMR with descriptive notation SCM.

The Fleet at Dover

PRIDE OF DOVER

Dover–Calais service: 1987 – 2010   **Year built:** 1987   **Builders:** Schichau Unterweser AG, Bremerhaven,
Germany

Gross tonnage: 26,433 tons   **Length(oa):** 169.60m   **Beam:** 28.27m **Passengers:** 2,290

Vehicle capacity: 85 x 15m lorries or 585 cars

Notes: The *Pride of Dover* was the first of Townsend Thoresen's 'Chunnel Beaters' which entered service in June 1987 following the P&O take-over in December the previous year. In September 1987 the fleet was rebranded P&O European Ferries after which she lost her distinctive orange hull. In preparation for the arrival of the *Spirit of Britain*, the *Pride of Dover* was withdrawn from service in December 2010.

PRIDE OF CALAIS

Dover–Calais service: 1987 – 2011   **Year built:** 1987   **Builders:** Schichau Unterweser, AG, Bremerhaven,
Germany

Gross tonnage: 26,433 tons   **Length(oa):** 169.60m   **Beam:** 28.27m **Passengers:** 2,290

Vehicle capacity: 85 x 15m lorries or 585 cars

Notes: The *Pride of Calais* entered service in December 1987 and her career has very much followed that of her sister ship. She is due to be withdrawn from service in preparation for the entry of the *Spirit of France* in September 2011.

EUROPEAN SEAWAY

Dover–Calais service: 2002-   **Year built:** 1991   **Builders:** Schichau Seekbeckwerft AG, Bremerhaven,
Germany

Gross tonnage: 22,986 tons   **Length(oa):** 179.70m   **Beam:** 28.30m   **Passengers:** 200   **Vehicle capacity** 120 x
15m lorries

Notes: The *European Seaway* was the first of what was intended to be a series of four identical freight ships for the Dover - Zeebrugge link and the only one remaining in her original configuration. With the closure of the Zeebrugge service in December 2002, she was switched to run Dover - Calais on a full time basis.

PRIDE OF BURGUNDY

Dover–Calais service: 1992   **Year built:** 1992   **Builders:** Schichau Seekbeckwerft AG, Bremerhaven,
Germany

Gross tonnage: 28,138 tons   **Length(oa):** 179.70m   **Beam:** 28.30m   **Passengers:** 1,420   **Vehicle capacity:** 120
x 15m lorries or 465 cars

Notes: Laid down as the fourth of the *European Seaway* quartet and intended to be the *European Causeway*, her plans were radically altered and she appeared as a passenger/ freight ferry for the Calais route, entering service in April 1993 and enabling P&O European Ferries to run their own 'Channel Shuttle' a whole year before the tunnel opened..

PRIDE OF CANTERBURY

Dover–Calais service: 2003   **Year built:** 1991   **Builders:** Schichau Seebeckwerft AG, Bremerhaven,
Germany but rebuilt by Lloyd Werft at Bremerhaven in 2002-03

Gross tonnage: 30,635 tons   **Length(oa):** 179.70m   **Beam:** 28.30m   **Passengers:** 2,000   **Vehicle capacity:** 120
x 15m lorries or 537 cars

Notes: Originally built as the freight vessel *European Pathway*, the ship entered service on the Zeebrugge link in January 1992. With the impending closure of the Belgian service, in April 2002 she was sent to Lloyd Werft at Bremerhaven for a complete rebuild on her original hull. She emerged as the *Pride of Canterbury* and re-entered service on the Calais link in May 2003. She replaced a ship of the same name which was formerly the Sealink Stena vessel *Stena Fantasia*.

The *Pride of Dover* was the first of P&O's 'Chunnel Beaters' designed specifically as her owner's response to the Channel Tunnel. In her day she also set completely new standards which have now been surpassed by the *Spirit of Britain*. *(John Hendy)*

The *Pride of Canterbury* was built as the freight ship *European Pathway* but was converted to passenger mode with her sister ship at Bremerhaven in 2002 - 03. *(John Hendy)*

P&O Ferries - The fleet at Dover

PRIDE OF KENT

Dover–Calais service: 2003   **Year built:** 1992   **Builders:** Schichau Seebeckwerft AG, Bremerhaven, Germany but rebuilt by Lloyd Werft at Bremerhaven in 2002-03

Gross tonnage: 30,635 tons   **Length(oa):** 179.70m   **Beam:** 28.30m   **Passengers:** 2,000

Vehicle capacity: 120 x 15m lorries or 537 cars

Notes: Originally built as the freight vessel *European Highway*, she entered service on the Zeebrugge link in June 1992. In December 2002, she officially closed the Belgian service and followed her sister to Lloyd Werft at Bremerhaven for a total rebuild, re-entering service as the *Pride of Kent* in June 2003. She replaced a ship of the same name, this being the former *Spirit of Free Enterprise* which was promptly sold to Greek owners.

EUROPEAN ENDEAVOUR

Dover–Calais service: 2007   **Year built:** 2000   **Builders:** Astilleros Espanoles SA, Seville, Spain

Gross tonnage: 22,152 tons   **Length(oa):** 179.50m   **Beam:** 25.24m   **Passengers:** 214

Vehicle capacity: 119 x 15m lorries

Notes: Originally built as the freight ship *Midnight Merchant* (the fourth of a quartet of vessels for service in the Irish Sea), in October 2000 the ship was instead chartered for use on the Dover - Dunkirk West route on which she remained until July 2006 when she was sold to Spanish owners and renamed *El Greco* for service from Barcelona. After purchase by P&O, the following October she was renamed *European Endeavour* for relief work on the company's Irish Sea and Dover Strait operations. .

SPIRIT OF BRITAIN

Dover–Calais service: 2011   **Year built:** 2011   **Builders:** STX Europe, Rauma, Finland

Gross tonnage: 47,592 tons   **Length(oa):** 212.97m   **Beam:** 31.43m   **Passengers:** 1,750

Vehicle capacity: 170 x 15m lorries + 195 cars (or 1,000 cars)

Notes: The English Channel's largest ferry to date, the ship is built to 'Dover Max' specifications and offers almost double the capacity of the vessel she replaces yet with a similar fuel consumption. She entered service in January 2011.

SPIRIT OF FRANCE

Dover–Calais service: 2011   **Year built:** 2011   **Builders:** STX Europe, Rauma, Finland

Gross tonnage: 47,592 tons   **Length(oa):** 212.97m   **Beam:** 31.43m   **Passengers:** 1,750

Vehicle capacity: 170 x 15m lorries + 195 cars (or 1,000 cars)

Notes: Built nine months after her sister, the *Spirit of France* replaces the *Pride of Calais* in the local fleet.

The *European Seaway* maintains P&O Ferries' Dover - Calais freight service and was the lead ship for a projected quartet of such vessels on the Zeebrugge link. *(Miles Cowsill)*

Purchased to supplement P&O Ferries' Irish Sea and Dover Strait freight services, the *European Endeavour* is seen leaving Calais.*(John Hendy)*

Acknowledgements

Acknowledgements

I would like to express my grateful thanks to all those people both ashore and afloat who have so willingly and enthusiastically given of their time in order to assist with the compilation of this book. Throughout the writing process, it has been very obvious that all at P&O Ferries in Dover have very much been aware that they have been involved in an exciting and groundbreaking project.

Particular thanks must go to the CEO, Helen Deeble and her Directors John Garner (Fleet), Simon Johnson (On Board Services) and Chris Laming (Communications) for all their support. Also at Channel House, my grateful thanks to Brian Rees (Communications) and particularly to Mike Langley the Programme Manager who was always there to assist and to answer any technical points concerning the new builds. Afloat, Captain David Miller and Chief Engineer Steve Stagg have also contributed to this publication and have shown willingness to assist, and courtesy and patience at all times which is greatly appreciated.

Alan Stewart of SMC is also warmly thanked for his input as are the Public Relations team at STX Europe, Rauma. Thanks also to those people that have supplied additional photographs, especially Brian Smith and FotoFlite, that have supplemented my own record of these two 'Ferries of the Future'.

Finally, my thanks are due to Miles Cowsill for his work in planning and designing the finished book.